"This wa

Dana's voice cut into Hal's euphoria. He froze. "Regrets already, sunshine?"

"Yes." She began tracing the line of his jaw, a winsome smile curving her mouth. "Now I know I'm never going to get enough of you."

His relieved grin warmed her. "You can have all of me you want," he drawled.

"What a promise," she teased. "Are you sure you know what you're committing yourself to?"

"I know what I'd like to commit myself to." He paused and brushed back a tendril of hair from her cheek. "I'll settle for a whole night of you . . . for starters."

Dana's stomach tightened with desire as she read the look in his eyes. When she spoke her voice was low and husky. "What about dinner? Aren't you hungry?" But she already knew he was. . . .

Thanks to Ed
whose love and support
carried me through the storms.
And thanks to Mom
for all the help and encouragement.

Love joins our present
with the past and the future.

                    Kahlil Gibran

Over the Rainbow

SANDRA LEE

MILLS & BOON LIMITED
ETON HOUSE, 18–24 PARADISE ROAD
RICHMOND, SURREY TW9 1SR

First published in Great Britain 1989 by
Mills & Boon Limited, Eton House, 18–24 Paradise Road,
Richmond, Surrey, TW9 1SR

© Sandra Lee Smith 1987

ISBN 0 263 76489 3

21–8904

Made and printed in Great Britain

Prologue

News Flash: Dateline, April 19, 1976

During the last sixteen hours, tornadoes swept across the Midwestern States leaving death and destruction in their wake. Three hundred people are believed dead. Oklahoma suffered the heaviest toll. The town of Clear Creek was completely leveled with thirty-five dead among the piles of rubble. Damage is estimated at over six hundred million dollars.

1

News Flash: Dateline, April 10, 1988

The national weather bureau reports it has lifted the tornado watch for Central Oklahoma as of six o'clock this evening. Residents are warned—

Dana Jean Cunningham's fingers shook as she switched off the radio. Twelve years ago, the same news station had canceled a similar storm watch. Dana had believed the report of safety then, but she didn't now. Total loss had taught her well.

Nevertheless, she turned down the bend in the hall and fled out of the basement and up the stairs to the lobby of Walkers' Lodge. The storm cellar had every modern convenience and design, but she hated to go into it.

Just then a deafening roar of thunder shook the lobby, filling it with an explosion of sound. Dana covered her ears with her hands. Shadows of tree branches danced across the floor as strobes of lightning flashed. She squeezed her eyes shut to block out the sight.

Suddenly a howling gust of wind smashed the door against the wall of the foyer. Dana turned with a startled jerk that slammed her frame against the electronic console. The dials and knobs of the stereo and intercom system pressed into her back, but she scarcely felt them. Her eyes were wide with surprise as she stared at the man who burst through the doorway.

Outside, lightning streaked across the gun-metal sky, leaving the acrid scent of electricity hovering in the air. Inside, rain drops fell from his yellow slicker, splattering the tiles.

Dana sagged with relief as the man secured the door against the noise. But the action didn't drown out the scraping of tree branches against the roof; the loud tapping sounded like a death march of loved ones lost in the cold night. She closed her eyes for a moment against the blue-green light still flashing through the windows and tried not to hear the thunder that ripped through the air.

Then, remembering the caretaker, she opened her eyes and called out, "Harvey?"

"Sorry."

It wasn't Harvey. His voice sounded too deep and vibrant. She had no idea who had just barged in, but at this point she welcomed anyone to draw her away from the edge of fear.

"Some weather."

Dana recognized the disgust in his tone, but she couldn't respond. She was paralyzed by a terror she didn't know how to control. Normally, she could handle danger well enough and the fact she was having so much trouble now, upset her. It had been many years since she'd been back to Clear Creek; she'd thought enough time had surely passed that she could face this. But she'd been wrong.

"Sure hope you have a room. We've been chasing this storm all day." He spoke while he shook back his hood. Wavy chestnut hair tumbled from the folds to slide across his forehead, and a few wet strands plastered themselves against his tanned cheeks.

"Any sign of a tornado?" Dana asked as she forced herself to straighten away from the console and walk toward the registration desk.

"There were supposed to be a couple, but the wind patterns never developed," he told her as he shed his rain gear and hung it on the hooks in the wall. He returned to the desk and shook his wet fingers before he began to fill out the registration form.

"You sound disappointed." Dana reached for the counter and gripped the edge. She didn't want the only customer for her aunt's lodge to see how much her fingers trembled.

"We've been trying for weeks to get near one. No luck though." He shrugged.

Dana stared in disbelief. He sounded like he wanted to see a tornado. Images clattered into her mind and focused; a windy stormy night, thunder rumbling with earth-shaking booms, lightning streaking across the sky, then silence...deafening, dead silence followed by a roar so loud she thought the earth was caving in. Snapping...like matchsticks, only they were two-by-fours, snapping all around. And running...running for her life.

"Miss?"

His voice called her back. Dana struggled to heed the summons.

"Are you all right?" he asked stepping closer. He leaned across the counter and waved his hand in front of her face.

Dana made an effort to appear normal. She took a deep breath and pulled together every scrap of her courage. She knew her behavior didn't befit her thirty-two years and she hated herself for it. She had her fear under control. She did!

"How long do you want to stay?" she quickly asked, but her voice trembled.

"I'm not sure. Depends on how the storm develops," he answered before turning the book back toward her. "You sure you're all right?"

She could feel his gaze probing her face. She had ignored his question about her welfare. Somehow it didn't seem right to tell a stranger who walked in, 'Excuse me, but I act like a fool when it's storming!' "I'll register you for the night and you can let me know tomorrow," she said in a businesslike tone, hoping she sounded composed. The pen made scratchy sounds as she filled out the form. Just then the brilliant glow of lightning flashed through the room. Dana dropped the pen. Immediately a deafening explosion shook the windows against their frames. Dana's ears ached from the burst of thunder. Her knuckles turned white from clutching the counter so tightly.

"The lightning's close, but we're safe inside." The man sought to reassure her, faint lines of uneasiness creasing his forehead.

Dana realized her reaction had revealed her fear. With effort she eased her fingers from the counter. He must not see such weakness. She despised women who fell apart when danger threatened. She could face any other peril with courage...anything but a tornado. Not for a second time.

"I don't usually act like this," she apologized. "I've lived in California for twelve years. We get rain, but not storms like this. I'd forgotten."

"They're wild all right." A smile tugged at his lips and a betraying glint of excitement brightened his brown eyes. She could tell he loved the clash of the elements. She understood. She had once felt that way herself.

"Aren't you afraid of quakes on the Coast?" he asked her.

"No." She hadn't known anyone who'd died in an earth tremor.

He must have sensed her bitterness. He changed the subject. "You related to George and Lillian?"

"I'm their niece. My name's Dana Cunningham," she replied. He was only trying to distract her, and she was willing to play along.

"Dana." His eyes lit up. "I've heard a lot about you. Name's Hal." He leaned back and studied her while he ran his thumb across the day's growth of beard on his chin. "Blond hair, hazel eyes—you look like a younger version of Lillian."

"Thank you," and Dana meant it. She admired her aunt's blend of style and elegance.

"Is George in the apartment?" he asked.

"They've gone to Florida. I'm managing the lodge for them."

"Georgina had her baby then?"

His excited question surprised her. He obviously knew the Walkers well enough to know about her cousin, Georgina. Dana peered at the registration book, Hal Underwood from Oklahoma City. His name didn't ring a bell.

He noticed her glance of curiosity. "I'm a friend of George and Lillian's. I met them several years ago."

They'd never mentioned Hal Underwood in their letters. Maybe he'd been a friend of Georgina's. Her attractive cousin had gone to university in Oklahoma City before marrying and she'd probably brought home lots of men.

"She had a boy," Dana told him.

"Great," he exclaimed. "I bet—"

Thunder interrupted his comment. Dana stared, her eyes wide and fixed in appeal upon his face.

"Say, you really are frightened, aren't you? It's only a thunderstorm."

Struggling to clear her throat, Dana tried to speak. She had to explain or he would think her a complete idiot for being so afraid.

"Twelve years ago a tornado hit Clear Creek."

"I know. It leveled the whole town."

"I was here," she whispered as a shudder tore through her. She didn't tell him that the tornado had killed her husband, Tommy, and year-old son, Sean. Some things were too painful to talk about.

"That happened a long time—"

Suddenly the door burst open with a bang and a gust of wind scattered papers everywhere. They were swirling in a spiral like . . .

"No!" Screaming, Dana backed into the corner of the room. She plastered herself against the walls in an attempt to disappear within the sturdy bricks. Vaguely, she heard Hal Underwood shouting, but she couldn't understand his words. The door slammed shut and she tried to focus on the man who had the strength to face the fury. The lights flickered and then went out.

"Not again," she screamed.

"Don't panic," Hal ordered as he searched in the blackened room for his way to her. A chair fell from the force of his body ramming into it. "Damn." He stooped for a moment to rub his shin.

Small frightened groans guided him to the corner where he had last seen her and lent an urgency to his steps. "It's just the lights," he soothed as he came around the counter. "The wind probably knocked down some power lines. There's nothing to be afraid of."

A catch of breath reached his ears. A flash of lightning revealed her holding her fist against her mouth to stifle her screams. He could see that she struggled against her fear and he guessed what it cost her. He had seen his buddies deal with terror during the war. He had helped George and Lillian and other townspeople through their first storms after the tornado of 1976. This woman was suffering a similar battle and he wanted to help.

"I'm coming," he continued to speak in a calming tone as he approached. "Talk to me."

He followed her wildflower scent and reached out. The silky fabric of her dress slid across his fingers, but before he could move thunder reverberated through the darkness and she threw herself against him. A muffled scream echoed and he felt her body trembling.

"Stop it, Dana." He reached up and grabbed her shoulders. They felt like they would easily snap in two, but he gave her a shake anyway. "You're safe."

He felt her hesitate with the shock of his rough treatment. She took a shuddering breath and he knew the hysteria had passed.

"I'm s-sorry," she stammered as she pulled back from him.

He could feel her muscles stiffening to brace her courage. In an instant of automatic reflex, he wrapped his arms around her and pulled her close.

"It's all right," he repeated over and over as he rocked her back and forth. With his face buried in the mass of curls, and her body fit comfortably against his, a hint of familiarity tugged at him. He felt as if he'd held her like this before.

Her heartbeat slowed and he realized his soothing was working. It gave him a sense of satisfaction to be her protector like this. Disappointed the storm had not produced any tornadoes, he'd come to visit with the Walkers during the lull before the next front moved in. Finding Dana instead, in a state of panic, had surprised him.

The swaying motion and her steadier breathing eased Hal's tension. He loved the excitement and power unleashed by a violent storm. But because Dana was so terrified, he decided perhaps he wouldn't tell her what he had been doing before his arrival. If thunder and lightning frightened her this much, she might not appreciate the fact that he chased tornadoes for a living.

Then again, he knew a lot about the weather. After all, being Oklahoma University's expert professor in the weather conditions of Tornado Alley, he could teach her about the elements. Understanding helped conquer fear. And besides, his talking would distract her.

"You can learn to love these storms, you know," he murmured into the tendrils of hair at her temple. "You just need to understand what they're all about."

She nodded and stepped closer.

"Thunderstorms develop when moist air near the ground clashes with warm air above," he rambled on. The deep hum of his voice echoed in the dark room. "That happens every spring when warm moist air rushes up from the Gulf of Mexico and meets with cool dry air from Canada."

"Are you going to give me a crash course in the weather now?" she asked, her breath warming his neck.

He could hear a trace of astonishment in her tone. Good. Maybe she'd come out of it.

"Just listen," he said. "From Texas all the way to Iowa and Indiana is where they have most of the thunderstorms. Oklahoma is right in the middle of the path."

"I know. That's why I live in California." She shifted and the action caused Hal an uncomfortable awareness of her curves, the firm muscles of her legs braced between his. He reminded himself that they were strangers.

"The worst has passed," he advised her as he tried to put an inch or two between them.

Raindrops no longer pelted the windows. Silence reigned in the darkness outside.

Dana knew she should pull away from his embrace. But now she felt . . . what? Safe? Yes, for the first time in twelve years she felt safe. His heart thumped steadily beneath her ear and he smelled masculine with the scent of the outdoors. She struggled with a longing to remain in his arms.

Dana tried to collect her courage and sanity. She couldn't. It had been a mistake to return to Clear Creek during the spring. Her aunt and uncle had needed her and she thought enough years had passed to erase the fear and pain. But they hadn't. It was clear now. She was not going to be able to face these storms.

"You've stopped shivering. Are you feeling better?" His voice echoed in the dark room.

"Yes, much," she murmured and took another deep breath. "We have candles."

"Where are they?"

"In a drawer under the counter. Over here."

A shiver tore through her when she pulled away from his security. She braced her courage against the chill. The search for the candles in the cluttered drawer brought slow degrees of sanity back to her jumbled senses.

"Here they are," she called out in triumph.

Before she could strike a match the door flew open for a third time. Again the wind gusted inside. Her heart thudded with alarm as heavy footsteps sounded in the shadowed foyer. Lightning flashed and outlined a burly man. Hal pulled her close beside him and kept his arm around her.

"Dana Jean, are you here?" A male voice hollered while its owner shut the door.

Suddenly the overhead lights flickered and glowed. Sheriff Kevin Blake stood with a flashlight in his hand and stared at Dana and then at Hal. There was an air of dependability, of steadfastness about him.

"You folks all right?"

Relief brought Dana tearing away from Hal's side and rushing to her friend. "The storm frightened me, but I'm all right now."

"Candy was worried about you and called." Kevin cast a penetrating stare from her to Hal and back again. "I decided to come check up on you."

"I'm glad you did. Would you like some coffee? It must be cold duty out there tonight."

"Can't. I've got to patrol the area. Another storm's due in a couple of hours."

Another storm. The thin layer of composure that Dana had managed to assume began to dissolve. Kevin had duty. Hal—would he stay with her? She had no right to ask him to.

"Candy wants me to bring you to her place to spend the night." Kevin told her. "She's got plenty of room in her storm cellar if tornado warnings come up again."

"I'll stay with you if you need to be here at the lodge," Hal offered, reminding her of her duties.

"I doubt there'll be anyone else coming in tonight," Kevin explained. His jaw tensed as if he resented Hal's interference. "Not with the earlier advisories against travel on these back roads."

Dana looked from one man to the other as they squared off in a clash of wills. A knife could cut the tension between them and Dana knew herself to be the cause. Yet, she could do nothing to ease the situation. She wanted to go with Kevin and stay with her friend Candy. But as temporary manager of the lodge, she shouldn't leave her customer to fend for himself.

The wind howled through the trees, knocking branches with a clatter against the roof to remind Dana of the harsh elements. Memories of her fear turned her blood to ice. She could not spend the night alone.

She glanced from one man to the other in search of an answer.

"Go on ahead," Hal urged. "I'm not going to stick around anyway."

"You're checking out?" She thought of him driving in the stormy night and knew she must put her responsibilities first. "You can stay here. I'll keep the lodge open."

"No. Don't do that on my account." He seemed to hesitate a moment. "I have to see about a few things down the road. I'll be back before morning and can let myself into my cabin."

His words did not ease her worry. No one should be on the highways tonight. She wondered why Kevin didn't forbid him to go.

"I'll take my key." Hal held out his hand and waited.

Looking from Hal to Kevin and back to Hal again, Dana shook her head. Both men had made up their minds and it was obvious there would be no point in arguing. A wave of exhaustion made her realize she didn't care anymore. She just wanted to be where she wouldn't hear or see the incoming storm.

Placing the key in Hal's palm, Dana paused. Warmth radiated from his fingers as he squeezed her cold hand.

"You'll be fine." He smiled and his confidence boosted her morale.

When he walked out the door, it seemed that he took an element of energy with him. Dana peered around at the emptiness of the lobby. For a fleeting moment, she remembered the secure feel of the stranger's arms. But the memory faded and her apprehension returned. With a sense of urgency, she checked to see that all the windows in the lobby were secure, then picked up the front door key.

"I'm ready, Kevin." She turned to her friend. "Let's go."

2

KEVIN DROVE the high-powered patrol car in silence. No words were needed to convey the support and friendship he offered. His quiet companionship had always been there for Tommy and, as Tommy's wife, it was there for her.

"I'm off duty at five in the morning." He broke the silence when they arrived in front of Candy's house. "Would you like me to take you back to the lodge then?"

Lights from the window beckoned. She and Candy had been best friends since childhood and Dana knew Candy didn't mind her staying. Still, she wouldn't want to impose any more than she had to.

"I should return early, but I hate to disturb Candy's family." Candy's husband, Bob, and his brother Ben Bradshaw, owned and operated the small town's only garage.

"Bob opens the station at six, so they'll be up and about." He reached over and patted her hand. "I'll pick you up and we'll go out to breakfast."

The gesture soothed Dana. Once again she realized how much she missed her friends of Clear Creek. During the three weeks since her return, the years had peeled away—years that had come between lifelong friendships. Big-city life could never offer the sense of belonging and closeness she felt in her old hometown. In the warmth of Kevin's gaze, Dana's earlier fear and tension began to ease.

"I'd like that, Kevin. I'll be ready." She opened the car door.

He smiled and waved before she shut the door and ran up the steps to the Bradshaw's home. She still hadn't become used to the modern look of the rebuilt houses in Clear Creek. But that didn't bother her now. She wanted to be inside—safe and warm with her friend.

Candy's hugs and welcome helped Dana forget the last upsetting traces of her ordeal. They went directly to the kitchen where the aroma of fresh-perked coffee greeted her. Already feeling better, she sat down at the maple table.

"I knew Kevin would bring you over." Candy bustled about, pouring hot steaming coffee and placing the mugs on the table. "I think he's definitely interested in our long-lost citizen."

"I'm not a citizen of Clear Creek anymore." Dana sipped her coffee, savoring the sharp taste and avoiding the reference to Kevin.

"Wouldn't you like to be?" Candy's brown-eyed gaze pierced Dana's wall of reserve. "You enjoy being back and we've all missed you."

Dana observed her friend over the rim of her mug. Candy still had a splash of freckles across her nose and long waves of golden brown hair. She looked much the same as she had when they were in high school. The only differences were small lines of experience and the steady assurance of maturity that reflected in her eyes. She appealed to that maturity now.

"I do miss Clear Creek and I love all of you." She paused while a shudder coursed down her spine. "But after tonight . . . I can't return. Candy, I was terrified when that storm hit."

"Oh, darling." Candy reached over and hugged her friend. "I should've thought of it sooner. Actually it was Harriet who did. She called from her cousin's farm. She'd been visiting or she would've turned up at the lodge."

For a brief moment, Dana wished Tommy's aunt had appeared. It would have saved her the display of emotion in front of Hal.

"How did Harriet know I'd be frightened?" Dana asked.

"We were all scared after the tornado," Candy explained. "Course for us that was years ago and we have control now."

"That's what I don't understand," Dana sent her friend a confused glance. "I thought by now it would be that way for me."

"But this was your first tornado watch since then— right? I mean, you don't have these storms in California?"

Thank goodness, Dana thought as she shook her head.

"Remember the letters I wrote? That first year, after the tornado, we were all basket cases. Project CARE even sent out a psychological counselor."

Dana remembered reading about how much the international relief organization had helped the citizens of Clear Creek. But she'd left so she hadn't received any of the counseling. Evidently she'd just buried the fears.

She listened with growing interest as Candy continued.

"Most of us had horrible nightmares. Even if the wind came up we'd be panic-stricken."

Dana remembered the nightmares. "I had those too," she whispered, more to herself than Candy.

"Course you did." Candy sat next to her. "You were afraid tonight. It's normal."

"And does it go away?" Dana's interest perked. "Are you still afraid when there's a tornado watch?"

Regret reflected in Candy's eyes. "Yes," she admitted, but straightened with immediate resolve. "But not like before. It's an inner fear—a warning—it just makes you kind of wary and alert. We don't hide anymore when there's thunder and wind."

"I'm glad to hear that," Dana spoke from her heart. "It was awful."

"Take this storm." Both women listened to the rain pattering on the roof. Occasional lightning flashed but no winds blew, not with the fury of the earlier storm. "I'm not afraid anymore. Are you?"

Dana considered for a few minutes. Candy's courage reassured her and suddenly she felt more confident. "I'm all right now."

"One goes on," Candy mused. "You just put your life back together and move forward."

"Which is exactly what I had hoped to do while I was here. I guess running away didn't do any good."

"Your leaving was normal too." Candy poured more coffee. "Many people left the area and never came back. At least you returned."

"But not for good," Dana warned. She'd promised to help her aunt and uncle. But when they came home, she'd leave and never set foot in Oklahoma again.

Candy sipped on her coffee while casting an assessing glance at Dana. Her next words caused Dana to shift uneasily in the maple chair.

"Kevin was talking about you the other day."

"He's been very sweet."

"I think he wants to be more than sweet." Meaning rang in Candy's tone.

Dana set her coffee cup down. She rose and began to pace the large kitchen.

"He's been out to see me several times in L.A." Dana confessed as she swung around to face Candy. "I think it was for Tommy's sake—you know—making sure I was all right."

"There's got to be more to it than that, 'specially after all this time."

"No." The idea was impossible. He was Tommy's best friend. That was all. Even if he was interested in her, Dana would never consider it. "I'm not getting involved with another Oklahoma man," she said with conviction. "Nor anyone else from the midwest."

Candy sighed. "No, I suppose not." Then her eyes twinkled merrily. "How about in Los Angeles? Got anyone there?"

Dana chuckled as she welcomed the lighter topic of conversation. "Tons of men," she lied. "I've got 'em scrambling at the door."

"I can see why. You're still good-looking—just like in high school." Envy glistened in Candy's eyes. "Tell me all about them. It'll perk up my day."

Laughing, Dana sat back down and retrieved her coffee mug. She had a lot of funny stories to tell and she made it sound like her social life was exciting. She did date often, but in reality she hadn't developed any close relationships. None of the men she'd met had inspired her.

During the course of her conversation, thoughts of Hal kept creeping up. Several times she was tempted to ask Candy about him, but decided against it. She wasn't sure if she wanted to explain her interest. They'd probably never meet again. She hoped *not* actually. How could she ever face him after such an embarrassing display of fear?

BY THE TIME Kevin delivered her back to the lodge the next morning, the storm had cleared. Blue skies and bright sunshine lifted Dana's spirits. With a song she'd heard on the radio echoing in her thoughts, she showered and prepared to face the day.

The bell rang, summoning service to the lobby. Dana hurried through the connecting apartment with a bounce in her step. A smile curved to form a dimple at the side of her mouth while her natural curls swirled in a golden mass around her face. One good thing about tending the lodge for her aunt and uncle, she thought, the customers were usually on vacation and in a good mood.

Located on the outskirts of Clear Creek, an hour's drive from Oklahoma City, the twenty cabins were filled most weekends. On weekdays, there were rarely over three or four lodgers at any one time. Later in the summer, the place would be jammed to capacity throughout the week, keeping her aunt and uncle in business. Fishermen wanting to test their skills in the nearby reservoirs made up the biggest percentage of their clientele.

The person dinging out a tune in the lobby was obviously in good spirits—probably an early-bird sportsman. Dana almost chuckled as she rounded the entranceway into the lobby. She halted midstride as she focused on her customer. It was Hal, confident and expectant.

At first, she enjoyed a rush of anticipation. But memories of the night spoiled her pleasure and she could feel her cheeks flush with embarrassment. Taking a deep breath, she tried to appear calm.

"Morning." He smiled.

Dana returned his greeting.

He stood, arms braced against the counter. Evidently he had returned to his cabin sometime during the night because he looked rested and freshly shaven. Although his buff shirt fit loosely, she could see the outline of hard muscle. Chestnut hair fell across his forehead, giving him a deceptive air of relaxed casualness. That impression disappeared with one look into his brown eyes.

He looked her over as closely as she had him. As if he touched her, she felt the trace of his gaze. It traveled from the tips of her red strappy sandals, up long legs that were accented by the tucks and pleats of her khaki jumpsuit. His brow raised with each of her curves, past the red belt showing off her trim waist, over her bust and to the slender neck framed by a standing collar and padded shoulders.

Reaching across the counter, he gave her dangling carmine earring a flip. "Amazing," he drawled, his voice husky and low.

From under heavy lashed eyelids, he looked straight at her and smiled. Dana inhaled a sharp breath as a sensation close to an electric shock charged through her. A laugh rumbled from his chest as he stepped back giving her space.

Dana struggled to regain her composure. "What's amazing?" She sounded normal, thank goodness.

"How much you look like Lillian." He referred again to her aunt. He held up his hands as if framing her face. "Only more golden—California tan, sun-streaked hair and amber flecks in your eyes."

Dana felt a tug of feminine response. Looking up she smiled. "My, my. Such flattery so early in the morning."

"I've heard a lot about you." His mouth curved into a mischievous grin. "I've heard all the tales of the trouble you and your cousin Georgina used to get into."

Dana cringed as she imagined what Uncle George, who loved to tease, could possibly tell this poor man. Dana had been born and raised in Clear Creek, Oklahoma. She and Georgina grew up as close as sisters. When Dana's folks had moved to Los Angeles during her senior year, Dana had stayed to live with the Walkers so she could graduate from Clear Creek High. Consequently, George and Lillian were as close as her own parents. "I take no responsibility for what George bored you with," she said with a grin. "He exaggerates."

"In this case he didn't." He studied her face.

"And you? Where did you grow up?" Dana asked, wishing to change the subject. "I'd guess it was Texas."

"My accent?"

She nodded and let him believe that was her only clue. In reality, she'd met other men with such charming arrogance and self-confidence and they were usually Texans. She figured he wouldn't appreciate that reference.

"I was born and raised in Houston," he admitted. "But my mother's family came from Oklahoma City. That's where I live now—in the house that was my grandfather's."

"Welcome to Clear Creek." She smiled while amusement danced in her eyes. "Are you staying longer?"

He nodded while he reached into his back pocket to pull out his wallet.

"Did you come to go fishing?"

"Most of the time I do. But not this time."

"No?"

"I just blew in out of the rain." He smiled and held out his credit card. "But I think I'll stick around. It's gotten mighty interesting in these parts."

His fingers brushed hers as she took the card. Her senses jammed; from excitement or apprehension she wasn't sure. She had to admit, though, that his presence sparked the morning with a bit more excitement than was usually found at the quiet lodge. He challenged her senses with his vitality. She could almost see energy bursting for release as he stood across the counter from her.

"How long are you staying?" he asked, shifting his stance.

No, she wouldn't react to the sight of him. She made a big production out of running his card through the machine as she answered his question. "Three more weeks."

A look of disappointment flickered in his eyes.

"I'd hoped they'd be gone longer."

"Whatever for?"

"It doesn't give me much time to get to know you." He smiled again, his eyes dancing with fun.

"That might be a good thing," she teased. "I could be a grumpy shrew for all you know."

"No way." He shook his head. "I know that much about you."

"From George's tales?"

"And the letters you send." He leaned against the counter, bracing his weight on his elbows. "I know that your favorite color is yellow, that you love steak smothered with mushrooms."

Dana placed her hands upon her hips, about to protest, but he went on.

"You like historical novels, light rock music, and Woody Allen movies."

"Those are superficial things. You don't know the important things," Dana interrupted. She felt like someone had opened her up, and it made her a bit uneasy.

"You mean like your work?" His eyes twinkled with merriment along with a hint of challenge. "I know about your supervisory job at Brockwell International and about how your division is working on the new compact airborne systems for business aircraft."

"Using Doppler radar," Dana murmured absently, stunned by the extent of his knowledge. She must speak to George about this. Some of the things she wrote were confidential.

As if reading her mind, Hal continued. "I know of all the men you date, but don't get serious with." He frowned and then his voice went quiet. "And I know that sometimes you're lonely—like me."

Silence echoed in the room as she stared. He had touched a sensitive nerve. Her husband Tommy had grown up with her and they had been in love as far back as she could remember. Replacing that void in her life had always seemed impossible. True, she had dated often and even tried to develop a serious relationship. But so far she'd never found anyone.

But this man seemed to be tugging on long forgotten senses. Impossible. She hardly knew him. Dana forced a laugh and straightened away from the counter and from Hal's magnetic pull.

"I won't be here long so I doubt we'll get to know each other well."

"You're wrong." His expression became serious as he reached across the counter to clasp her hand in his. He gave her a slight tug and brought her close. "I'm going to get to know you very well."

Her heart raced while her fingers burned within his. She pulled her hand away and forced herself to ignore the tingles he caused. "I'm not interested in complications or a relationship." That wasn't entirely true, but for as long as she was in Clear Creek, it was.

Unconcerned by her lack of enthusiasm, he continued, "Don't be so sure. Maybe I'll change your mind. You might even want to stay awhile."

Dana eyed him closely, wondering how much he knew about her past "There's no way I'll be staying. I have my job to return to. And speaking of jobs I have work to do now." She handed him his card and with a dismissive nod turned toward her aunt's apartment.

Hal watched her retreat, admiring the straight line of her back and the graceful swing to her walk. He smiled to himself, unaffected by her flat-out refusal to consider his options. Convincing her might not be easy, but he would. His steps were buoyed with confidence as he walked out the door.

The decision to remain in Clear Creek had surprised him as much as it had her. But thinking back, he understood the cause of his impulsiveness. Last night she had been frightened and vulnerable, but this morning he had glimpsed a vivaciousness and earthy sensuality that intrigued him.

Hal was sensitive to his own needs and he wanted to get to know Dana. He recognized that fact the instant she'd entered the lobby. His remarks had been bold but he'd caught the flickers of response in her eyes. It would certainly be worth pursuing.

Hal whistled as he strode to his van. He opened the back compartment to check on the array of scientific equipment displayed inside. His race across the back roads of Caddo County last night hadn't done the sensitive instruments any good. While he figured out his strategy to interest Dana, he could go over the gear.

Anticipation and pride swelled, as it always did, when he worked with the tools of his trade. The storm last night hadn't developed, but when tornadoes hit...

Nothing excited him more than the thrill of adventure and daring. He loved the storm chasing and although he'd say it was dedication to his research, deep down he knew the danger lured him as well. His teammates were the same; a breed of men set apart by their courage, trying to come to terms with the puzzle of the tornado.

Hal wondered how much his occupation would interfere with his pursuit of a relationship with Dana. Perhaps she'd never find out. After all, the locals called him "the professor" in reference to his position at the university. That would be enough for her to know.

He looked out of the van to see her approach the Walker's station wagon, as though thinking of her had conjured up her person. Sunlight had tangled in the riot of curls framing her face. His heart thudded at a faster pace when she returned his wave with a smile. He shook his head and forced his muscles to relax so he could finish his work.

The sputters of an engine not turning over brought him back out of the van. He tried to stifle his pleasure. Her car wouldn't start. Now was his chance to be a hero.

"Looks like you might need a ride," he offered as he neared her car.

"What's wrong with it?"

"I'm not a mechanic, but I'd guess it was out of gas."

She frowned. "I haven't filled it since I arrived." Self-disgust sounded in her voice.

Hal bit the inside of his lip to keep his expression serious. "Come on. I need to buy a couple of things at the drug store so it won't be any bother."

Before she could protest, he took hold of her elbow and guided her out of the station wagon and into his van. Dana watched him with interest as he drove the large vehicle.

"What do you do in Oklahoma City?" she asked.

"I'm a professor at Oklahoma University."

Dana eyed him closely as recognition began to dawn. Vague memories of George's reference to "the professor" were beginning to form. He had been around to help the townspeople rebuild after the tornado. That explained his close relationship to the Walkers.

But a professor? She eyed him again and shook her head. Her visions of George's professor didn't come close to the real thing. She had pictured a short intellectual sort with glasses and rumpled hair; not someone who looked like he belonged on the centerfold of *Playgirl* magazine.

"I'm beginning to recall George mentioning you." She noticed his pleased expression.

The drive into town was short, and during that time he told her a little about his job. He also mentioned briefly his huge Victorian home, which he had completely refurbished and modernized. Before he could elaborate further, they arrived at the post office where Dana had been headed in the first place. Jack Crendall, the postman, stopped her to say hi after she picked up the mail, then they headed for the Drug Emporium. There, she knew their errand would be delayed, because Tommy's Aunt Harriet owned the drug store.

Harriet's plump arms wrapped around Dana in a tight hug. The long-ago familiarity of the rosewater scent in Harriet's graying hair brought back a flood of memories. Dana returned the affectionate embrace and stepped away.

She began to introduce Hal only to discover he knew Harriet well. The older woman was naturally friendly, but Dana had never seen her wrap a bear hug around a stranger as she did Hal. Seeing them act with such genuine affection lent a touch of poignancy to her mood.

Returning to Clear Creek three weeks ago had unleashed a Pandora's box of emotion. Within Clear Creek's boundaries, were all her childhood experiences of happiness and love. Adjusting to the strangeness of the rebuilt town proved difficult, but the physical features didn't really matter. The people in it made up the hospitable charm. Nothing could compare to small-town fellowship, and Dana realized how much she missed it.

"Thanks for calling Candy last night," she told Harriet. She shifted, uncomfortable with the memory of Hal's presence. "I didn't do well."

"It's to be expected, missy." Harriet stated, too practical to give in to sentimentality. "You'll soon get over it. We all manage fine now."

"Thank goodness I won't have to. Hopefully we won't have another storm before I return home."

"Home," Harriet snorted. "L.A.'s not your home. It's about time you came to your senses and came back here."

"I can't do that." She grasped Harriet's arm and squeezed, all her pent-up fear and dismay evident. "There's nothing for me here anymore."

"We'll see," Harriet insisted, and a knowing glitter reflected in her eyes. "There's nothing like your roots to pull you back into the fold."

After Hal made his purchases, they left the drugstore and Harriet followed them outside. They paused to view the rebuilt town. As if the small community had had a face-lift, everything seemed fairly new and modern. After living in Los Angeles, Dana wasn't bothered much by the concrete and glass that had replaced the quaint wood structures. It was the lack of trees that disturbed her most, the fact that all the giant cottonwoods that shaded the streets of the sleepy town were gone.

"What's that new building down there?" Dana asked as she spotted the strange structure.

"That's the new fire station," Harriet explained with pride in her voice.

Dana's glance swept down the main street. Nothing familiar stood in her line of vision. Only memories and the people.

"We'd better go." Hal broke into her thoughts.

"Don't be in such a hurry," Harriet scolded Hal, but she didn't attempt to delay them further. Leaning towards Dana, she placed a kiss upon her cheek. "I'll stop by at lunchtime and catch you up on all the latest news."

"Sounds fun." Dana waved as Hal guided her toward the parking lot.

"Good to see you, honey," Harriet shouted after them.

Hal helped Dana onto the bench seat of his bronze van. "That Harriet, she'll talk your ear off."

"I know and I love it." Dana chuckled as the truth of that statement lightened her mood.

"She knows everything that's going on," Hal agreed with an affectionate note in his voice. "She's better than a local newspaper."

No one minded Harriet's tales. They were never malicious nor cruel. She simply had an avid interest in life around her.

Hal drove through town and slowed at the intersection on the outskirts. "Are you game for a detour past the reservoir?" he asked. "It would only take us another twenty minutes or so."

Dana glanced at the road that led to the lodge and then back at the longer route that wound through the rolling hills, along one side of the lake and then back to town in a circular loop. Hal's expression beckoned and she shrugged. Why not? After all it was supposedly her day off.

"Are you anxious to check out the fishing spots?" she teased.

"Just finding an excuse to spend time with you." He smiled and it sent unexpected shivers down her spine.

She started to protest but before she could, Hal had shifted gears and headed the van toward the lake. Dana tried to focus on the sunny day and rolling terrain instead of the man beside her. It was difficult to do. Her glance kept sliding over to catch glimpses of sunlight glistening in his hair. Or the play of movement in his forearm as he turned the steering wheel. Or the way his long legs stretched in front of him.

The interior of the van was comfortable but Dana began to feel heated. She hoped he couldn't hear how her breathing pattern had changed.

The lake came into view and Hal stopped the van at a vista point on top of a knoll. He held the door open for her, and Dana thankfully left the vehicle and stepped outside. The cool air was refreshing, but her relief was shortlived. Hal came around the front of the van and stood close beside her.

"I love this view." His arm brushed against hers.

"There're lots of boats." She pointed below to break the contact. The image of his arms around her last night came to mind. She focused on a brightly colored sail-boat. "Do you have a boat here?" she asked.

"I have a bass boat I keep at the marina. Would you like to go out in it?"

Dana quickly shook her head. "No. I won't have time."

"Don't tell me you don't fish?" He looked at her in mock surprise.

"Sure I do. Dad used to take me all the time, but I haven't been out on the reservoir since he moved to L.A." She stepped away from him, glad to remember the fun times with her family. "You see, George doesn't like to fish." Neither did Tommy for that matter. "We spent our spare time soaring." She glanced up and spotted a glider inching upward on a thermal. Hal's gaze followed hers.

"Do you ever go soaring with George?" she asked, thinking he must have. Soaring was one of the main attractions in the small tourist community.

"Since I have the boat, I'm usually in it all day."

He had a strange look on his face as he watched the glider. It made her wonder why, but she dismissed the question. She didn't really want to know anything more about this man.

"We'd better head back. I told Harvey I'd only be gone for a bit," she told him.

"Sure." Hal swung his gaze back over the lake and then one more time to her. His look of male apprecia-tion made her melt a little inside. He held out his hand and she let him lead her back to the van.

On the drive back to the lodge, Dana thought about Hal. It was too bad she hadn't met him in Los Angeles instead of here at Clear Creek. He was the kind of man she could really like. But she wouldn't let herself be attracted to Dr. Harold Underwood. He brought embarrassing moments of last night's fear to mind, not to mention an appeal that could prove too tempting.

3

WALKERS' LODGE looked much the same as it had before the tornado. In spite of the newness and the latest storm-proof construction, George had managed to recreate the country charm that had made his lodge special. The decor was simple and rustic. The main building that housed the Walkers' living quarters as well as the lobby faced the colorful compound. From picture windows in the homey sitting area for guests, one could see the log cabins that surrounded the grounds. Dana stepped out of Hal's van and looked at the setting. George had planted pine trees around the perimeter and bright flowers lined the walks to the fenced swimming pool area.

Harvey waved a greeting from the lobby door. He'd been with the Walkers as long as she could remember. A few more lines in his craggy face were the only changes she noted. Harvey was more than a caretaker. He was the Walkers' right-hand man and occasionally managed the office if the owners were gone for a few hours.

"What's up, Harvey?" she greeted him with an affectionate hug. Her senses were keenly aware when Hal joined them. Wasn't he going to give up and leave her alone?

"Just wanted to remind you that I'll be watching the place today and tomorrow—Monday and Tuesday— the same as usual." He nodded toward Hal. "That'll give you time to see your young friend here."

"He's not—" Dana began but Hal interrupted.

"That'll be great, Harvey."

Dana swung around, annoyance bringing out the green tints in her eyes. Hal had been following her around all morning. Friend or not of Uncle George, the lodge business didn't concern him.

"Don't you need to unpack or something?" She didn't bother to keep the slight vexation from her voice.

He smiled, unconcerned by her tone. "It won't take long. I suppose now's as good a time as any."

He pulled the cabin key from his pocket and with a gleam in his eye, leaned closer and murmured in a husky voice, "I'll see you shortly."

Not if she saw him first, she thought. She watched his progress until he disappeared into his quarters.

"Always liked that man." Harvey nodded towards Hal's cabin. The comment warned Dana of the strength of his charisma. Harvey didn't take a liking to many people, especially outsiders.

"George mentioned he helped them after the tornado," Dana probed.

"Helped lots o' folks." Harvey nodded and rubbed his grizzled chin. "He was passing through when the tornado hit."

That news surprised her. She wondered if she'd seen him that fateful night? Could that be why he seemed so familiar? No. She'd remember—wouldn't she?

"You go on and rest now." Harvey started toward the Walkers' private quarters. "Lots o' your friends plan to stop by today, and tonight's the picnic."

"I can't. I have to get caught up on the books and make next week's schedule for the cleaning crew."

"I'll take over for you this afternoon then, for the big shindig," he relented.

"Thanks, Harvey." Dana reached over to pat his worn cheek.

After finishing in the office, she decided to do her chores in the apartment. The place showed signs of neglect after her stay at Candy's. Dirty dishes were piled in the sink and the living room looked untidy. With her usual efficiency, she began to straighten up. She had finished the kitchen and was in Georgina's former room making the bed when footsteps sounded in the apartment.

"Dana?" Hal's voice carried down the hall.

"I'm busy. I won't be able to visit for a while," she hollered and then did an about-face and hoped he hadn't heard her. Housework bored her and Hal definitely didn't. "Never mind, come on in."

"You almost done?"

She could hear his approach as he came down the hall and stopped. His presence permeated Georgina's room as his body filled the doorway. His woodsy after-shave blended with his unique male scent. She tried not to let him know how glad she was to see him.

"Would you like something cool to drink?"

"Sure." He stepped back and allowed her to pass. His knowing grin alerted her that he was aware of her reaction to his closeness.

Dana skirted between the round oak table and sideboard and paused to see if Hal followed her. He looked at home in the casual setting of her aunt's kitchen. Auburn glints shone in his hair, matching the copper pans hanging overhead. His movements were fluid and coordinated, indicating a well-toned physical condition.

"Beer or iced tea?"

"Beer's fine." He took the icy can she offered and straddled one of the oak chairs. Dana felt her tension mount as he relaxed.

"Don't you have to teach classes at the university?" she asked. Most universities held classes on Monday.

"I only instruct during the fall semester," he informed her. He took a swig of beer and smiled. "During the spring and summer I do research."

"This is research?" Dana lifted her shoulders and gestured toward the lodge.

"No," he chuckled, apparently unconcerned by the direction of her probing. "I'm taking personal leave."

"Must be nice." She leaned against the counter, her hands upon her hips. His presence sent her senses scattering, but she wasn't going to let him know that—at least not if she could help it.

"That's the advantage of my schedule. It's flexible—gives me a chance to take care of my personal needs." He tipped the chair on two legs and leaned back. His glance never left hers.

What a lead-in. She wasn't going to be so foolish as to ask him what his needs were, although she could tell he wanted her to. It was a struggle to keep a straight face, but she managed and asked about his work instead. "What research project are you working on?"

He hesitated and then shrugged. "The weather. I'm a meteorologist."

"So that's why you gave me that lecture last night?"

"Can't help it—instinct to teach, I guess."

Interest showed in her expression as she continued to question him. "So what's the big project you're doing now?"

His gaze shifted from hers and he began to trace the logo on the beer can. "Just collecting data."

Was that avoidance in his manner? "For what?"

"Stuff in general."

Definitely avoidance. She eyed him with a curious glance, which he ignored. Dana's mind raced with possibilities. Obviously he wanted to keep it a secret. Maybe it was a government project.

With a thud, he brought the chair down on all four legs. "So, back to the reason for my personal leave. How about a picnic or a drive in the country?"

Her heart picked up its earlier fast pace. "You took leave to go on a picnic?"

"I took leave so I'd have time to be with you."

No. This was all wrong. Part of her was flattered by his pursuit. Part of her even craved it. But she didn't want to lead him on with false hopes.

"I can't. I'm working."

"It's your day off."

"Look, I have lots to do here and I'm expecting several friends to drop by."

"And you want me to leave you alone."

"Yes." His easy acceptance of her problem brought her a moment of relief, but it died with his next move.

He tossed down the last of his beer and stood. Slowly he came to tower beside her. Dana pressed against the counter, but he gave her no quarter. He braced his hips on the tile and leaned forward until mere inches separated them. Her throat constricted. "I'll let you get back to work for now."

Dana peered at his firm lips, hypnotized by their movement.

"But I'd like us to work on getting to know each other."

"And if I don't want to know you?" Dana managed to respond.

"You will," he promised with a mysterious smile. "I'm going fishing. You take care, y' hear."

Before she could respond, he pulled away and disappeared from sight. Dana stood, frozen in place. He'd been so close and it occurred to her that she hadn't really minded.

A female voice pulled her attention away from her scattered thoughts. Thank goodness. Friends were arriving and their lively chatter would dispel her body's yearnings.

Dana welcomed the women she'd grown up with as they paraded through her door. Every time she'd seen them these past three weeks, she'd marveled at how little they'd changed over the years. Lines in faces added character and some carried a few extra pounds, but overall they were the same friends.

Harriet arrived later and behaved with her usual no-nonsense attitude.

"Howdy, girls," she greeted them before giving Dana a hug. Seating herself on the sofa, she said, "Tell me quick, everything I missed before I got here."

"A lot," Candy assured her as she placed her coffee cup and saucer on the maple end table. "We were just reminding Dana of all the trouble she used to get us into."

"No need to tell me a thing. I can remember those days like yesterday. See these gray hairs?"

"Come on, Harriet, we weren't that bad," Dana insisted as she poured coffee for the newcomer and refilled everyone else's cup.

"You were the worst, missy. Always trying the latest fad and wanting to do something new and different. I never could figure where you came up with all your ideas."

"Her imagination." Candy smiled, disrupting the alignment of freckles on her cheeks. "Dana always had a wild one."

"Plus she was the brave one," another friend piped up. "She always tried things first and then if she didn't get in trouble, we would go ahead and do it."

"Yeah. Thanks a lot," Dana chided. "Don't think I didn't notice at the time."

"No chance. You're too quick on your feet," Harriet teased.

"Remember when she wore the miniskirt?"

"I was too afraid to try it. I'm glad Dana did it first."

"Especially since she got called in by the principal."

"Remember Miss Fogurty?"

Laughter filled the cozy living room, bringing back a flood of memories. She and her cousin Georgina had often entertained these same friends.

"Come off it." Dana leaned forward in the large recliner as she tried to calm the group. "I'm a changed woman now—mature and sensible."

"Humph." Harriet let her opinion of that news be known. "Mature and sensible, yes. But being a big fancy supervisor requires a bit of daring and courage."

"I—"

"That's right." Candy joined in after passing a bowl of nuts. "You're the only one of us who had the nerve to go off and live in the city."

"That wasn't nerve. That was foolishness," Harriet informed them.

"No, it wasn't," Candy said in defence of her friend. "Dana looks terrific. She left, got a college degree and a job. That took guts."

Yes, it had taken guts to move to the position she had on her job, but courage had nothing to do with why she'd left Clear Creek. She wondered what her friends would think of her bravery if they'd seen her trembling and cowering during the storm last night. Maybe Candy had already told them.

Remembering last night brought a new wave of images that were not entirely unpleasant—an easy smile, a comforting shoulder to lean on and the soothing tones of a deep voice.

Candy's next question penetrated her thoughts. "What time you coming to the picnic?"

"Later this afternoon. I have a few things to finish up here at the lodge before I leave."

"We're having it just for you."

"Just like the old days?" Dana asked, as pleasure filled her.

"You bet," Harriet chuckled. "You know us, any excuse for a party."

"I can hardly wait," Dana assured her. "I started some homemade chili to bring."

"Your cooking still as good as it used to be?"

"Better."

The women chattered on for another half hour before taking off to get ready for the big get-together. As she waved goodbye, she noticed the sunny weather, hot and humid from the rain. She looked forward to the chance to see her friends again and enjoy their easy companionship.

Hal came to mind. No doubt he'd be there, too, and it annoyed her how much that realization intrigued her. Thoughts of him kept popping into her head far too often for her comfort. It wasn't just his presence; she kept remembering things like how it felt when his arms wrapped around her and how his breath had feathered her curls.

Dana gave herself a shake and returned to her duties in the lodge.

THAT AFTERNOON, laughter and friendly banter drew Hal to the volleyball court in the park's center. Harvey had told Hal that he would find Dana playing there. Sure enough, there she was, joining in the game with ease.

Her hair shimmered in the late-afternoon sunlight like molten gold. A red halter top and jogging shorts barely covered her lithe body. A shaft of desire sent a sudden jab to his loins as he admired her.

He stood back and observed for a few minutes before joining the group. In spite of her long absence, he could see that Dana belonged. Teasing references to past incidents came readily to the lips of the other players. She was comfortable with her friends.

The ball went out of bounds and Dana chased after it. She looked up and her glance rested upon him. Hazel eyes clouded for a passing second and then cleared. It wasn't the greeting he wanted, but at least she had reacted to the sight of him. It was a beginning. Hal started toward the group.

"Which side is winning?" he shouted. "I want to be on that team."

"Hey, Underwood," Bob Bradshaw hollered out, "come help us show these animals who's the best."

"You're losing, I take it," Hal said while peeling off his tennis shoes. The heat in the grains of sand penetrated the soles of his feet.

"We won't be now that you're helping out," Bob responded.

Amongst jeers from the opposing team and encouragement from his fellow members, Hal joined the melee. There was no question about his welcome in the game. Several times during the past few years, he had accompanied George and Lillian to various gatherings. The citizens of Clear Creek enjoyed his presence, even though he was not quite one of them.

Glad that he had changed into shorts and a tank top, he stepped up to the spot beside Dana. "Looks like I came at the right time," he commented, enjoying her reluctant smile. It sent sparks of hope to charge his energy.

"It's a big bash to welcome me home."

"I figured they'd pull one off for you."

"So that's why you came—" She placed her hands on her hips and glared at him with teasing glints in her eyes. "—to crash the party."

"You bet." He chuckled while positioning himself for action.

"Catch any fish this morning?"

"They're ready for breakfast," he bragged and couldn't help puffing up with pride.

"You two going to gab all day or are we ready to play?" Candy hollered from the other side.

The game began and Hal participated with unusual zest. To his surprise, he realized his enthusiasm stemmed from showing off his skill to Dana. Like a thirty-eight-year-old rooster, he chided himself, strutting around to attract her attention. But it worked, so who was he to get all self-conscious about it?

"You're a good player," she told him after he'd just made a smashing spike.

"Popular college pastime. You're not bad yourself."

"I live near the beach in Santa Monica," she said with a casual shrug. "There's always a game going on."

Her comment made him curious about her social life in L.A. How close was she to the men she'd mentioned in her letters? The ball whizzed right past him and he cursed his preoccupation. The ribbing from his fellow players didn't rub quite so badly when she flashed him a forgiving smile.

The game continued with their side making more points to even out the score. He paused a moment to wipe the sweat from his brow. The breeze cooled his temperature but fired his insides when it carried traces of Dana's flowery scent toward him. Her skin glistened in the springtime heat, making him want to savor the salty taste of her.

Suddenly, the ball sped to a spot between them. Both he and Dana jumped for the spike and sent the ball spinning for a point. The impact of their collision left them sprawling in the sand.

Concerned for Dana's safety, Hal rolled over swiftly to remove his weight from her. His flesh burned where he'd made contact. Her well-toned muscles felt firm, yet her skin was soft.

"You all right?" He was gasping from the exertion.

"I think so." Laughing, she sat up.

He began brushing the sand from her shoulders and back until she turned to stare into his eyes. His fingers paused to rest on her shoulders while his gaze locked with hers. Her eyes were more brown than green today and he felt himself drawn into their depths. The rest of the players seemed to recede into the distance.

Her tongue traced her bottom lip and Hal forgot about his audience. Longing welled up to swamp his good sense and he leaned over to kiss her. When he neared, close enough to feel her breath heat his skin, she pulled back. A look of surprise reflected in her eyes and Hal smiled.

"I never could resist temptation." He tried to make light of the attempted kiss.

She nodded toward their companions with a mischievous glint in her expression. "Maybe they'll help change your mind."

Hal looked up to see every pair of eyes questioning him. "Oh, oh," he murmured, while hefting himself to his feet.

He reached out a hand to assist Dana and caught the humor from her throaty chuckles. "Guess I'll have to behave," he said with a shrug, while he let her know with his eyes that he had no intention of doing that.

Her breath caught, he noticed with satisfaction. She pulled herself up with ease and quickly moved away from him. But her hesitancy didn't disturb him. The local folk would not be around all of the time.

DANA SAT under the picnic table awning, out of the evening sun. The breeze and a cold beer had cooled her off after the vigorous game. Thanks to Hal's talent, their team had won.

Looking over at where he stood talking to Bob and Ben Bradshaw, she wondered why he pursued her. She had to admit she didn't really mind his attentions. They flattered her ego.

The light breeze tossed the layered waves of his chestnut brown hair. When he'd leaped in the air to drive a powerful spike, she had sensed the unleashed power within him. His movements were steady and calm, yet there lurked a restlessness beneath the surface as if he were ready to take advantage of any sign of action. She would have to be careful to keep their relationship light. In spite of the fact that in three weeks she'd be gone, he claimed a strong pull upon her senses.

"Well, well, Dana Jean. You look pretty as ever." At the familiar male voice, Dana turned to see Kevin Blake standing behind her. Quickly she stood and gave the sheriff a kiss on the cheek.

"Where've you been?"

He returned her welcome and smiled his easy grin that sent memories tumbling in her head.

"Upholding law and order," he quipped.

"It's hard to imagine. After all the mischief you and Tommy used to stir up. I can't believe you're on the right side of that badge," she teased.

Tommy and Kevin had been inseparable while growing up. Tommy had missed him when Kevin had gone off to join the Navy after their high school graduation. She often wondered if Tommy envied his friend who had pursued his dream to travel while he had stayed home to marry Dana.

"All that gave me practice." Kevin chuckled. "There isn't anything that the kids can put over on me. I've done it all."

"A real terror, huh." She gave him the title, but knew better. The Walkers had praised Kevin's strict but fair attitude toward law enforcement. "Guess I'll have to behave while I'm here."

"You'd better," he agreed, but then pretended to grow serious. "Maybe I should keep a close eye on you though. Wouldn't want you exposing our fair community to big-city corruption."

"Kevin Blake," she scolded. "Since when could *I* corrupt anyone in this town."

"Never know." He shrugged and then she saw the mischief gleam in his blue eyes. "Maybe I just like keeping a close eye on you."

Laughter welled up and Dana leaned over to give Kevin a quick hug. She couldn't help but notice how his arms lingered around her a little longer than necessary. It also occurred to her that this wasn't the first time. Candy's words came to mind and she began to wonder if Kevin felt more than friendship for her. Impossible. They'd been like brother and sister.

She leaned back and noticed the blond hair curling from under his hat. While not as exciting as Hal, he had a comfortable appeal. She stepped away, embarrassed by the trend of her thoughts. An automatic reaction had her glancing around in search of Hal. He stood apart, near the Bradshaw brothers, staring hard and intent at Dana's hand still in Kevin's. She couldn't help the slight touch of defiance. She tightened her fingers a shade and kept them there.

"Don't you two make a fine pair?" Candy's observation came as a welcome diversion.

"I've just been warned by the law to keep in line." Dana laughed.

"You better believe him, too," Candy warned with mock severity.

Out of the corner of her eye, Dana caught the steady movement of Hal's approach. The nervousness it caused in her made her uncomfortable.

"You going to spend the rest of the evening here?" Dana asked Kevin with hopeful interest.

"I'm on duty until eight. But I'll be back. Harriet told me you fixed your chili."

' "The way to a man's heart," Candy mocked lightly. "Kevin, you are an easy man to please."

"That's my motto," Kevin admitted.

The laughter attracted the attention of their other friends, who began to crowd around. Dana welcomed the growth of the group. Candy's husband, Bob, stepped up to enfold his wife in a loose embrace. Ben brought up the rear with several other young people in tow, until the crowd got rowdy with jokes amidst the light banter. Dana reveled in the sense of belonging and companionship.

Hal joined in the group, but more as an observer, chuckling at the kidding and agreeing with good-natured humor to the comments. It pleased her that he appeared to enjoy her friends. Most people would feel inhibited by the tight-knit togetherness of the towns-people.

Dana was so wrapped up in the fun that she didn't see the approach of the woman behind her. It startled her when the feminine voice wailed in a plaintive tone. "Dana Jean. You're back again?"

She turned, only to be enveloped in a phony hug. Heavy perfume assailed her as blond curls brushed

against her face. Dana pulled back to look at Sharon
Lewis, Tommy's older sister.

"Hello, Sharon." Dana cast her a wary glance and
then smiled at Sharon's husband, Jim. He stood back a
few paces with an apologetic look on his face. She
hadn't seen her sister-in-law since her return, but then
Dana hadn't sought her out. They'd never gotten along.

"You poor dear. Coming to town must bring back
memories of Tommy." Sharon's gushing words stilled
the boisterous rowdiness of the crowd.

Several people began to shift with unease and Dana
understood. Sharon's reminder of Tommy was inap-
propriate.

"Sharon, don't." Jim came up from behind and pulled
his wife back.

Dana sensed the uncomfortable restlessness from her
friends and eased from the group to join Sharon. With
Jim's help, they wandered to a private spot among the
picnic tables.

"I've adjusted," Dana told her sister-in-law. A heavy
sigh of regret escaped her lips. How many times had she
faced this battle? "It's been so long that—"

"Not that long." Sharon flared while angry sparks
gleamed in her blue eyes. "You just come back and you
laugh and flirt as if nothing happened."

Pain shot through every cell of her being at Sharon's
cruel words. Dana didn't know how to respond to the
anger and bitterness.

"It's been twelve years." Jim reminded his wife in
soothing tones. "It's time to forget. Let Dana live her
life."

"Have you found a replacement for my brother?"

"Sharon!" Jim warned in firm tones.

Dana stared. Jim eased his wife away from the picnic area with gentle persuasion, leaving Dana alone to recuperate from the assault. Before she could recover her sense of reality, Sharon's son accomplished what Sharon had not.

Jason, his blond curls bouncing, ran across the lawn and caught the football. He waved while he flashed a toothy grin. Freckles sprinkled across his nose and dimples creased his tanned cheeks.

Dana's heart turned over. Jason looked exactly like his uncle at fifteen. He had Tommy's lanky build and bright-eyed intelligence. But it wasn't the thought of Tommy that paralyzed her. *Sean*. Her son would have been thirteen this year and playing football with his cousin.

Would the pain never end? Most of the time now she didn't hurt. But moments such as these would rise up from the past. She had to get control. Dana took a deep breath and returned to the crowd. She tried to focus on the jests that were bandied back and forth, but her concentration was shot.

"Hey, storm chaser, did you catch up to a big one yet?" Bob was saying.

It took a moment for Dana to realize they were talking to Hal. She glanced up and saw that he was staring hard at her. She summoned a smile and succeeded. "Storm chaser?" she asked.

He shrugged. "Can't help it if I love to go out in the rain."

Everyone laughed.

Dana wasn't quite sure what they were all chuckling about, but then she'd missed half of the conversation. Hal leaned toward her and whispered. "It's my nickname. They think I'm nuts about storms."

"Are you?" She knew she was still missing part of this interchange.

"I'm nuts about you." He wiggled his eyebrows up and down.

This time Dana's laugh was genuine. "You're a nut, all right."

His look of mock hurt made her chuckle again. It felt good. She didn't even mind when he inched his body closer to hers. The warmth from his suntanned skin chased away the earlier chills. The deep tones of his voice filled some of the emptiness. His easy manner relaxed the tension inside.

Hal stayed by her side for the rest of the evening. She couldn't help but enjoy the attention. He brought her a heaping plate of food and served her with a bow. It didn't even faze him when Bob and Ben Bradshaw started in on him.

"Don't wait on her, now," Ben warned.

"She'll be expecting service forever," Bob concurred.

"It wouldn't hurt you to pick up a few pointers," Candy commented and then smiled prettily. "I'd love another helping of Dana's chili."

"Do you see what you've done, Underwood? You've set a bad example." Bob groaned but he didn't hesitate to fill Candy's plate.

Candy sent a conspiratorial wink to Dana and sat back, looking pleased. Dana had to turn her head to keep Bob from seeing the grin on her face. When she'd managed to control it, she swung back around. On the way, her gaze clashed with Sharon's. Blue eyes glared.

Dana stiffened and tore her glance away from the accusing stare only to find Hal studying her.

"Something wrong?" he asked in a quiet voice.

For a fleeting second she let him see the ache. She wanted to lean against him and say yes. Bob's hearty laugh from across the table brought her out of the trance. She shook her head. "Everything's fine."

He didn't believe her; she knew from the way he glanced away from her, over her shoulder in the direction of Sharon Lewis and then back again. "Are you finished eating?" he asked.

She nodded. The thought of another bite of food almost made her choke.

"Come on." He didn't give her a chance to decide. Instead, he clasped her fingers in a firm grasp and pulled her up. They said their farewells as they gathered their plates and belongings. Then he guided her toward the parking lot and murmured, "Let's go for a ride."

4

HAL STOPPED beside the Walkers' station wagon and reached out his hand. "Do you have the keys?"

Dana dug in her pocket and handed him the set. "Where's your van?"

"Harvey dropped me off. I figured I could come home with you."

Dana knew she should be annoyed with his presumptuousness. It even crossed her mind to mention she might have gone home with Kevin or someone else for all he knew. But she hadn't. Suddenly, she was too tired and drained to make an issue out of nothing. She scooted across the seat to the passenger side while Hal slid in behind the wheel.

Before they arrived at the lodge, he pulled off on a turnout at the top of a knoll. "The sun's setting. Shall we watch it?"

Colors were already beginning to streak across the sky. "It's going to be a good one," she said, settling down to lean her head against the back of the seat.

"What happened tonight?" His deep voice broke the silence.

"What do you mean?" She knew what he meant, but she stalled with the question.

"You were having such a good time until Sharon Lewis showed up. What was that all about anyway?"

Dana could feel the last traces of the good mood that she'd clung to so tenaciously finally slip away. She could picture Sharon's icy glare, she could still see Jason tearing across the field. She released her breath in a long sigh.

Hal reached across the space separating them and pulled Dana to his side. She tried to move away from the security and safety of his arms, but he positioned her across his lap. His warmth melted all of her resistance. She curled against him and let his male essence surround her.

"I'm so tired of this aching," she said, speaking from her heart.

"What? Tell me what hurts," he whispered while brushing his lips against the tendrils of hair at her temple.

The caress calmed her. It wasn't sexual or threatening. It was caring, from a friend. Dana rested her head against him and let herself respond to his support.

A feeling came over her that she'd been here before, been comforted by these same arms and same deep voice. A shudder raced through her as she dismissed the thought as impossible.

"Dana." Hal shifted her in order to place his fingers under her chin and tilt her face to his. "Tell me what's wrong."

"You really don't know?"

"Does it have to do with the sadness in your eyes?" He traced a finger across her brows. "I've seen it before and it returned when Sharon was talking to you."

Her heart became heavy as she considered his words. Was her pain that obvious? Her family had been aware of her occasional depression, but they understood the cause.

Why couldn't she let it go? After all this time she shouldn't still hurt. It made her angry at herself to be so vulnerable.

Slowly, she dropped her hand from his face to rest upon his chest. Unaware of her actions, she began to toy with the chestnut strands of hair that lay above the tank top. Her mind struggled with her inner battle.

Should she confide in Hal? Yes. Perhaps when he knew the truth, he would leave her alone.

Dana inhaled a deep breath and began. "Sharon is my husband's sister."

Hal stiffened but Dana barely noticed, except that her hand froze. She continued. "Tommy and I were childhood sweethearts and we married right out of high school. Sharon always resented our marriage."

Dana settled her cheek back into the crook of Hal's neck. Once again her fingers weaved in and out of his chest hair in an unconscious release of emotion. A peacefulness settled and grew as she spoke. "She thought I held Tommy back. Right away we were tied down." A picture formed of their baby and their joy. No, Tommy hadn't resented the responsibility.

"But he's dead now."

She tilted back and looked at him in surprise. "You *do* know about it."

"No." He shook his head and brushed back tendrils of hair that the breeze from the open window had tossed across her face. "Only that George mentioned once that you were a widow. He never told me who or when. I always wondered. That part of your life has always been a closed book as far as your aunt and uncle are concerned."

"It's their pain also," Dana sighed. "No one wants to be reminded of accidents and death."

"But Sharon spoke of it," Hal said and Dana sensed a protective anger in his tone. "I don't know her very well, but I can't imagine anyone being so insensitive to your feelings as to bring it all up again."

Hal placed her head back onto his shoulder while he absently rubbed the tense muscles of her neck. The soothing massage sent warmth to chase away the chills. Dana responded to each sweep of his strong fingers with trust.

"She says it's my fault he died." How many times had she accused herself? If she'd been the one to get Sean when he cried; if she'd not listened to the weather report. She moaned and buried her face closer to Hal.

"Do you blame yourself?" His astuteness jarred her senses enough to still the threatening tears.

"Yes. So many times," she confessed. "Then I tell myself that it wasn't my fault."

She saw the muscle tic of reaction in his jaw but went on. "I keep repeating the same words over and over."

"Then don't listen to Sharon anymore. Don't let her upset you."

Dana stared at Hal. He didn't understand. The truth made her throat tighten and threatened to choke her as she forced out what she must say.

"It wasn't just Sharon who upset me. It was Jason."

"Jason Lewis?" A puzzled frown formed on Hal's forehead. "What'd he do?"

"Existed."

"He looks like Tommy did when you were growing up?" Hal guessed with partial accuracy.

"Not just that." Dana pulled back to watch his reaction. "Our son . . ."

Hal's eyes widened as his grip tightened on her arms. His gaze searched and she let him see the true source of her agony.

"He should've been playing in that field with his cousin. He should be laughing and living. . . ."

Hal released her arms to capture her wrists and pressed her hands against the wild beat of his heart. "Dana, I'm so sorry—I didn't know."

She shook her head. "I'll go back home. Forget this hell."

"Will that help? Will it ease the pain?." His voice was gentle, persistent.

"No." She froze like a statue and tried to gather inner strength. Fearing defeat, she let her head drop. Wisps of hair fell forward to hide her features. "I've got to overcome this. I must put the past where it belongs."

"Is there any way I can help?"

"It's something I have to do myself." She took a shuddering breath. "I had hoped that coming back here would make a difference. At least I admit that there'll always be a place in my heart for Tommy and Sean. But it's in a far corner now. I need to make room for more."

"You will, Dana."

"Yes, I want that." She nodded as hope welled; hope and pent-up longings for another taste of life. "Help me, Hal."

He let go of her wrists and placed his hands on either side of her face. With gentle care he tilted her head and she could see the sincerity in his gaze.

His tender touch unleashed a flood of yearning within her. When she stared into his eyes, her mind began to spin and her heartbeat raced. She wanted all that he promised, all that he offered.

As if sensing her desperate need, he paused. "Dana, are you sure...."

"Yes," she whispered as her hand slid from his chest to wrap around his neck. "Kiss me," she demanded before she pulled his head down to hers. He met her halfway and pressed his lips to hers.

Hunger consumed her as she tasted the desire in his kiss. His fingers tangled in her hair, then moved down her back. Dana pressed against his strength. She locked her arms tightly around his neck and sought to rekindle her lost passion. Her system jolted to a sense of aliveness she hadn't felt in years, while all rational thought fled her mind.

She explored him with all of her senses. Her tongue sought the salty taste of his skin. She enjoyed deep breaths of his woodsy male essence. Her fingers explored the strong planes of sinew and muscle as she traced his bare shoulders.

He shuddered and her heart soared. Could she give him the same pleasure he gave her? She pressed kisses down his jaw to his neck and rejoiced in the erratic beat of his pulse. A moan escaped her lips as desire washed over her.

"Dana," he groaned. Her kisses were setting off a storm wilder than any he'd ever experienced. Her touch proved to be everything he'd dreamed, and more. He wanted her, here on this knoll under the prairie sky.

But not like a teenager in the station wagon.

Even if their location had been better, he wouldn't take her. Too soon, his mind railed at him while he fought the urgings of his body. She was too emotionally upset now. It wasn't the time. Somewhere in the heat of passion, rational thought functioned. He wanted her to trust him. He'd meant what he'd said when he promised to help her. It occurred to him how much he needed to relearn the lesson of love himself.

Her lips returned to his and he stole a few more moments. He drank in her sweetness and savored the honey taste of her mouth. He explored the dark secrets with his tongue and let desire flood his senses.

Just before he drowned, he gathered every ounce of his strength to pull away. He grasped her arms and tugged with gentle persuasion. The puzzlement in her eyes tore at his heart. He took a deep breath of the clear spring air.

"Not here—not in public like this."

She stiffened and a slight flush darkened her cheeks. When she started to pull away he stayed her with a careful hold.

"Stay with me for a few minutes," he advised. "We'll watch the sunset while we cool down."

Without giving her a chance to protest, he pulled her beside him and settled her head upon his shoulder. He remained silent until he felt her body begin to relax. They viewed the splash of colors that were brightening the horizon. Purples, reds and fiery orange ignited the sky, just as their bodies had flamed scant minutes earlier.

"I'm sorry." Her voice carried into the quiet surrounding them.

For her outburst or for her kisses, he wondered. "There's nothing to be sorry for."

"I never fall apart like that," she told him and he could hear the regret. "Nor do I . . ."

"Sh, sh." He didn't want her to apologize for her passion. "Sometimes it helps to clear out those pent-up feelings."

"I suppose," she sighed. "But it makes one feel like such a fool when it's all over."

Hal chuckled in friendly reassurance. The last thing he'd consider this woman to be was foolish. He told her so and after that she settled beside him. Hal watched the streaks of color trace across the sky while her breathing steadied.

Questions tumbled around in his mind. But he dared not ask for fear of upsetting her again. When had she been married? How did they die? The tornado crossed his mind, but he dismissed the possibility. He figured she would've still been in high school.

She'd mentioned accidents. Had there been a fatal car crash? Most likely, since both her husband and son were killed. Had she been in it—driving? He recalled her blame for surviving.

When he'd first realized she was widowed, before he'd known of a son, he had assumed her husband had died in the war in Vietnam. Why he'd made that assumption, he didn't know, except perhaps because of his own experience of being there and seeing the death of so many of his buddies. He shuddered at the thought of long-forgotten horrors.

"Are you getting cold?" Dana lifted her head to peer at him.

"No, just the past," he told her. "Like you, I needed to put my life back together again, and strangely enough, it was here in Clear Creek that I finally managed to do so."

She turned her head to see his face. "Tell me about it."

Hal hesitated, reluctant to dredge up painful memories. He searched her eyes and when he saw her sincerity he knew he could tell her. Perhaps it would help her find the courage to fight her own battles. He took a deep breath and began.

"I came back from the war in pretty ragged shape."

"Vietnam?" she interrupted.

He nodded and he saw her expression soften with empathy. It encouraged him to go on. Until that moment he hadn't realized he feared her reaction. For years, he'd tried to come to terms with the public's scorn of the Nam veteran, and deep down he worried she might have reacted like his ex-wife.

"I was married before I left, and I came home expecting sympathy and help in healing the emotional scars."

Hal paused as bitterness and pain tore at him. His life had become an angry torrent of hatred at that time. It had definitely soured him on the idea of marriage.

"She left you while you were away?" Dana asked, bringing his attention back to her. He reached up to smooth away the frown that lined her forehead.

"It would have been better if she had." He stared but didn't see her. His mind focused on the image of Peggy, dark-haired, dark-eyed and dark-spirited. "She was there to welcome me home all right. But she was angry and she accused me of being a warmonger. You see, she'd become a peace activist."

"She didn't consider your feelings?" Dana looked indignant. "Surely she knew you were doing what you thought right."

"No." Hal gave a sad shake of his head. It hadn't taken long for him to realize he'd never loved or understood Peggy. She'd been a dream that had kept him going through his horrible existence in the jungle; a dream that turned into a nightmare.

"It wouldn't have hurt quite so much if it'd just been her, but the whole country seemed to share her view."

"That's not true." Dana sat up to emphasize her words. "Many people supported—"

"I know that now." He brought her back down beside him. Her nearness helped the telling of his tale. "My parents understood."

Their backing hadn't meant nearly as much as his grandfather's. Still alive at the time and living in the old Victorian home that was now Hal's, the old man had sat for many hours and talked with his grandson. His counsel had become especially helpful after the tornado in Clear Creek that changed Hal's life. Hal continued talking, wanting to explain it all.

"At the time I focused on the negative things. Hatred brought me down more surely than a bullet."

"And what changed that?"

"Strange as it seems, it was the tornado that wiped out Clear Creek. Gramps and I came out here to go fishing at the reservoir. When the storm hit, we headed for town and found everything gone."

Hal stiffened as the horror of that night washed over him. He didn't notice that Dana tensed also, clenching her fists while her face turned ashen.

"When I saw the suffering of all those people, I realized my self-pity was a waste. I decided then and there to do something worthwhile with my life."

He fell silent as he recalled the battle he'd waged with his inner self. He'd returned to Texas, where his folks lived and he had grown up, and earned his doctorate in meteorology. Then he moved in with his grandfather in Oklahoma City where he applied for a position at Oklahoma University. But his position there wasn't his main interest. Every spring and summer his time was spent with the team of storm chasers he headed in the region.

The storm chasers, a group of scientists from the National Severe Storm Labs in Norman, had only one goal: to track down a tornado and put a portable weather station in its path. It was the only way they had to gather the information needed to learn about the tornadoes. The data was compared with the Doppler radar readings in the storm lab where tests were made to learn how to predict accurate tornado warnings; warnings that could have saved the people at Clear Creek years ago.

The danger and challenge of facing the wild twisters while they tried to place electronic sensors in their paths quenched Hal's thirst for adventure. The data they collected to learn how to predict the destructive winds satisfied his need to find purpose in his life. If he could prevent another community from being demolished, he would consider his life worthwhile.

Before he could tell all this to Dana, a car drove by. It must have been friends from the picnic because they honked.

Hal groaned inwardly at the interruption. He didn't want to give up the intimacy they shared. "Looks like we'd better head back." Hefting himself upright he reached over to offer a hand to Dana.

Her fingers gripped his and he was tempted to pull her against his body for a quick embrace. He steadied her with his hand instead.

The look of disappointment in her eyes gave him hope. Later they would continue to get to know each other.

THE NEXT MORNING Dana couldn't stop thinking about Hal. Kissing him had awakened dormant needs and desires. While she welcomed the awakening, she resented the fact that it was happening here in Clear Creek.

Being back in the homey small-town environment pulled at her loneliness. But under no circumstances would she return to Oklahoma. She was tempted by Hal's magnetic appeal. She was flattered by his caring and she was challenged by his wit. His appeal was a threat to her safe existence, and Dana was afraid.

The sound of a motor vehicle reached her from the parking area in front of the lodge. Dana peered out the window to see Hal's van pull up. A skip in her pulse set her on edge.

Hal slid his long legs out of the van and stretched. Dana watched his movements, feeling both a mixture of resentment and pleasure. Sinews knotted beneath the sleeveless yellow T-shirt. Blue jeans hugged the tight curve of his buttocks and legs. Hunger assailed her senses and she turned away from the sight.

Quickly she stacked the receipts from the guests who had just checked out. "These are the rooms that need cleaning today." She handed the list to the young woman working the morning shift.

Dana watched the maid's hurried strides to the laundry room and paced. She looked forward to seeing Hal and she dreaded it. Friends, she decided. They could be friends in the three short weeks she had left. Imagining more would be just that—pure imagination.

He entered and greeted her with a sensuous drawl. "Hello, sunshine."

Dana's heart fluttered at the endearment and her breath caught at his smile. His hair flopped across one brow and brought out the brandy color of his eyes.

"I've missed you this morning." He leaned against the registration desk and brushed a light kiss across her lips.

Dana stood transfixed. All of the sound advice to herself that morning flew out of her head. Her lips tingled and her heart raced. She wanted more kisses. "Did you go fishing again?" she finally managed to ask, glad her voice sounded steady and calm. "One of our guests said they were biting."

"No, I was checking out some of the equipment I have in the back of the van."

Dana didn't remember seeing anything during her ride with him, but recalled there had been a curtain separating the cab from the interior. "What equipment is that?"

"I needed to test the radar probes." He selected a nearby chair and sprawled in it with his long legs outstretched. "They're sensitive and get jostled bouncing in the van."

Her interest perked up. "What kind of radar do you use?"

He looked at her for a moment with a puzzled line across his brow. He seemed reluctant to tell her, which she thought was odd. Finally he spoke. "I'm a meteorologist, remember?"

"So it's for monitoring weather patterns?"

"That's right." He motioned to the chair beside him. "I'll give you a tour later, but for now come sit and talk to me. There aren't any customers this early, are there?"

As if in answer to his question an elderly man entered the lobby. Fluorescent lures dangled from his battered hat.

"Where's a good place to eat, young lady?"

"A half mile down the road, Mr. Frys. There's a small café with the best home cooking around."

When he'd shut the door behind him, Dana cast a glance at Hal. He gave her a good-natured smile and patted the seat beside him.

"Come on. You can take a break now."

Dana chided herself for being so pleased with his invitation. As she settled in the chair, she straightened her teal slacks and matching camp shirt. She knew the dark blue flattered her golden coloring, so Hal's admiring glance didn't surprise her.

"You must use Doppler radar," she commented, glad to have something to talk about besides her traitorous feelings. "That's what we turn out at Brockwell."

"Tell me about the new airborne system," he invited, evidently more interested in learning about her career than disclosing his.

She basked in the warmth of his gaze while she told him about her work.

"What made you go into that field?" he asked later.

"I didn't plan it," she admitted. "I started out as an assembly worker in the beginning. Brockwell is near my folks' house." She'd taken the first job she could get her hands on when she arrived in L.A. and had worked long numbing hours.

"I only had a high school diploma," she recalled, her gaze distant as she spoke. "I soon discovered I needed more challenge, so I began working my way up. At night I went to U.C.L.A. and earned my degree in management."

"Congratulations. That's tough, working and going to school at the same time."

"It took me eight years," she confessed. "But I have a good job now."

"Doesn't sound like you had much time left for a social life."

She noticed the interest he had in her answer. It perked her vanity which she tried to ignore. "There was enough," she shrugged.

"Speaking of social life." He shifted. Faint traces of his scent drifted her way. "What're your plans for the day? Harvey mentioned you have it off."

"He's not taking over for me until this afternoon. I have a few things I need to do around here."

"Can I help?"

"No." His offer amused her. Surely he had better things to do.

"What about this afternoon?"

"I promised to help Candy put up some strawberry jam." She hoped her voice didn't sound as disappointed as she felt. Canning preserves was a springtime tradition she had been looking forward to. But now...spending an afternoon with Hal definitely sounded more appealing. You're better off, she reminded herself.

"Isn't that usually a community project?" he asked.

"It ends up that way." Dana stood and went to straighten a wall hanging that had tilted. "All the women who can get away come over and pitch in."

"Everyone helps out then?"

"Anyone who wants some of the jam." She turned and smiled. "I'm taking some back home with me."

"Sounds like a plan. Wouldn't mind having some myself." He rose and came close.

Dana's pulse fluttered. Her voice trembled. "I guess I could spare a jar."

"Well now," he drawled as he leaned forward and braced his hand on the wall behind her. "I figure I better do my share of the work then."

"But..."

"Surely you aren't going to tell me that's woman's work?" he scolded.

"No—I mean..." She paused to take a breath. His nearness was flustering her. "It'll be all women there and I'm sure—"

"They wouldn't mind an extra pair of hands—especially to lift heavy pots?"

"'Course." She backed up against the wall. He followed. His eyes were full of fun.

"I get it," she said. "The odds—one rooster in a house full of hens."

"You sound like Harriet."

"No." Her hair feathered her face as she shook her head. "*She'd* say there was a fox in the henhouse."

He gave her a wolfish grin. "I'm only interested in one chick."

He swooped down to place a quick kiss on her lips. Her body responded immediately and she started to reach for more. But he stepped away and waved goodbye. "Finish your chores. I'll pick you up at noon."

It took a second to come back to her senses. Just as he walked out the door, she recovered and hollered after him. "Make it eleven-thirty."

He saluted.

The morning flew or so it seemed. She had a hard time concentrating on the mundane chores. Her mind was too busy thinking about Hal and trying to picture him in Candy's large kitchen.

Actually he fit in well.

"Ready for the next batch?" he called out over the heads of Candy and Harriet who were busy at the table pouring thick jam into hot jars.

"Bring it over," Dana told him. She wiped her fingers on the apron covering her terry-knit top and shorts and quickly grabbed the wooden ladle.

"Here it comes."

His muscles bulged against his T-shirt when he lifted the huge pan off the stove. Dana stared. She couldn't help it. He looked so good as he made his way around the table and set the bubbling jam on the counter.

"More sweets for the sweet." He straightened with a pleased look on his face.

"You get cornier by the minute." She shook the ladle at him.

"And you love it, missy," Harriet chimed in. "Best idea ever to have a man around. Why didn't we think of it sooner?"

"Careful, Harriet," Candy warned. "You're gonna make his head swell."

"No chance," Dana began skimming the foam off the jam. "He's already loaded with confidence."

"That's not the problem," Candy's sister, Susie, informed them as she sliced more strawberries.

Dana looked up in time to see Hal steal a couple of ripe red berries from Susie's basket. "Harold Underwood," she scolded.

"Guilty." He sauntered toward her, his grin full of mischief. He stopped in front of her and popped a juicy berry into her mouth. "I'm willing to do time—just so long as it's with you."

A dozen women of varying ages whooped and teased with that remark.

"You've been out chasing too many storms," Candy told him. "You've lost your head."

"Nope." He crossed his hands on his chest. "It's my heart I've lost."

"Good grief." Dana shook her head in mock dismay and returned to her chore. But inside a warmth settled in her heart. "What am I going to do with you?"

"I've got several good suggestions."

"Which we'll ignore." She set the spoon down. "For now you can set this pan on the table for Harriet and Candy."

"Yes, ma'am." He bowed before he lifted the heavy pot.

Just as he set it down, the back door slammed open. Thinking it was one of Candy's children, Dana didn't look up to see who'd entered.

"Well, well. I guess you don't need *my* help."

At the sound of Sharon Lewis's voice, Dana stiffened. She hadn't even thought about the fact that her sister-in-law would come. She'd never joined in when they were younger.

"Come on in," Candy offered. From the look of surprise on her friend's face, Dana guessed Sharon's visit was unusual.

"I was going to help this year, but I changed my mind." Sharon tilted her nose into the air. Her accusing glare aimed at Dana and Hal instantly created tension in the room. But suddenly the awkward silence was shattered by a loud crash.

Dana swung around to see Harriet doubled over. In a flash, she rushed to her side. Hot jam oozed across the older woman's hand and arm.

"Move, quick." She guided Harriet to the sink and at the same time issued orders. "Candy, get some ice! Susie—a towel! Hal—start the van!"

"I'm all right." Harriet tried to insist, but she was helpless under Dana's fast action.

In minutes, Dana had Harriet sitting in the van while she crouched beside the woman to be sure she didn't go into shock. At the same time she gave Hal directions to the clinic in the neighboring town.

THE WEATHERMAN POINTED to the satellite maps and predicted storms for the next few days. Dana didn't pay much attention. She was too tired from worrying about Harriet.

Hal stood up and turned off the blaring television. They were the last couple left in the stark waiting room. As silence settled, Dana sighed with relief. She'd long ago become accustomed to the antiseptic smells of the clinic, but the noise from the television and crying children had worn on her nerves.

"It shouldn't be much longer." Hal sat down beside her in the plastic molded chair.

"Do you want more coffee?"

He shook his head. Dana could see lines of fatigue around his eyes. It had been a long wait.

She reached over, grabbed his hand and squeezed his fingers. "Thanks Hal, for all you've done."

"I care about Harriet, too, you know." His thumb caressed the back of her hand.

"Yes. It was a bad burn, but I think she'll be all right."

"Thanks to you." He brought her hand to his lips.

Her skin tingled where he touched. She suddenly longed to curl up in his arms. "I didn't do much."

"You acted fast in an emergency." He sounded impressed.

Dana glowed. After the embarrassing first impression he had of her the other night, she was glad that he had a chance to see she wasn't a complete ninny. Of course it was unfortunate that it had been at Harriet's expense.

"When we get back to the lodge I'll fix you a big dinner," she offered.

"That's not necessary. Besides—" his face became serious "—I'll be checking out."

Dana stiffened.

"I have to take care of some business."

"I see." Pulling her hand from his, she stood and began to pace. So much for taking a leave to spend time with her. She stepped to the window and focused on the partial rainbow on the horizon, not wanting him to see the disappointment in her eyes.

5

THE WEEK SPED BY and Dana didn't hear a word from Hal. She tried to convince herself that it was for the best, but she couldn't stop feeling somehow cheated. At least the weekend crowd had kept her busy.

Today she had time off, and she couldn't help but remember last Monday and Tuesday when Hal had been trying to convince her to spend time with him. She wasn't going to mope, she promised herself that. It was a waste.

She dug in her closet and found a pair of cotton parachute pants and a loose-fitting sweater. Just as she finished changing into the rust-colored outfit, the phone rang and she ran to answer it.

"Lillian. It's great to hear from you. How're Georgina and the baby?"

Dana smiled as her aunt bragged about her grandson, but her smile disappeared when Lillian got around to the real reason for her call.

"You want to stay in Florida two more weeks?" She gripped the receiver. "'Course I can get the time off. Don't worry about it. You and George enjoy your visit."

She hoped she sounded more convincing than she felt. Two more weeks in Clear Creek? She wanted to refuse to stay, but her aunt and uncle hadn't had a vacation in ages. And they sounded so happy.

"Everything's fine here," she said reassuringly, "Yes, it's been lovely weather. It's sunny and breezy right now."

Fortunately the storms predicted for last week had tracked to the east and missed Clear Creek. Would her luck hold out for two extra weeks? She doubted it.

"Goodbye, Lillian. Give my love to everyone and a big kiss for the baby."

Dana frowned as she hung up the phone. The day wasn't starting out well at all.

"That's the best news I've heard all week."

Dana jumped at the sound of the drawling voice behind her. She spun around to see Hal leaning against the doorjamb of the apartment's connection to the lobby.

"Harvey said you were up and about. He let me come on through."

The sight of him—so sure of his welcome—left her breathless. He had on blue jeans and a sweatshirt and looked expectant and ready for action. Dana bristled. She didn't like the fact her pulse had picked up its pace and she didn't want to be so happy to see him.

"What brings you here?"

"You, of course." He peeled away from the doorway and walked toward her. "We're going to get to know each other, remember?"

"Kind of hard to do that when you're gone for a week."

He paused and Dana scolded herself for letting him know how much it mattered. She tried to appear nonchalant, but she knew he saw through her.

"You missed me, didn't you." His grin widened. He swooped her up and swung her around. In vain Dana tried to touch her toes to the ground as she braced her hands upon his shoulders. She really wanted to lean against him and give herself up to a long kiss.

Finally he set her down, but he didn't let go of her waist. "I missed you too. I was called out of town."

"It doesn't matter," she lied.

"Sure it does. I was going crazy thinking I was losing a whole week. Now, thanks to your aunt and uncle, we've got more time."

Her heart began to pound when he lowered his head to kiss her, but before he could, a horn honked in front of the lodge. Dana pulled away and tried to tell herself she was glad for the interruption. The horn sounded again. A worried frown formed on her brow.

"That's Kevin."

Hal stiffened.

"He's come to pick me up."

"Oh?"

Was that disappointment as well as wariness in his eyes? Oh, for heaven's sake. Knowing she'd regret it later, she asked him with a hint of annoyance, "Want to come along? I'm going soaring. Kevin has a plane and can tow me up."

"In a glider?"

"It's a two-seater."

"I'd rather we stayed here—just the two of us." He moved toward her.

Her heart skipped a beat at the sultry tone in his drawl. It would be so easy to agree. She stepped back.

"We've already reserved the glider."

He heaved a sigh of resignation. "What do I need?"

"Do you have a jacket? It gets cold at the higher elevations."

"It's in the van. I'll go get it."

After Hal left, Dana scrambled to collect her gear and lock up the apartment. He had come back. She shouldn't be so glad. She tried to calm her growing excitement as she hurried over to the pick-up where Kevin waited.

"Mind if Hal comes along?" she asked.

Kevin's smile disappeared. "There's room." He didn't quite hide his displeasure.

Dana studied his familiar features and decided maybe it was a good thing to have Hal along for Kevin's sake as well as hers. It would help her to keep her relationship with both men on a casual basis.

With that decision made, she climbed into the cab of the pick-up and scooted to the middle. Hal tossed his jacket behind the seat and settled beside her.

"Have you been soaring before?" she asked Hal, trying not to notice his shoulder pressed against hers.

"No." He stuck his arm out of the window to give her more room.

"You've flown, though?"

"A chopper—in Nam." He didn't elaborate and Dana decided to drop the subject when she noticed the sudden grimness in the set of his jaw.

"Kevin's dad used to fly crop dusters. You were thirteen when he taught you to fly, weren't you Kevin?"

"Twelve." His answer was as curt as Hal's.

A slight tension began to build. These two weren't going to hold up a conversation—that was for sure. Dana fell silent for the rest of the drive.

At the small airstrip on the outskirts of town, Hal waited patiently while Dana and Kevin made arrangements to rent the glider and set it up for towing. He couldn't believe he'd agreed to go in such a flimsy looking aircraft—with no motor besides.

He cursed. He'd been so relieved that Dana had invited him along, that he hadn't stopped to think about where she planned to take him. His stomach muscles tensed. Could he pull it off? He hadn't been in the air since his chopper had crashed in the jungles of Southeast Asia.

What he really wanted to do was drag Dana back to his cabin and make love to her for the rest of the day. It had been all he could do not to kiss her when he'd seen her so earthy and sensual in the morning sunlight.

This last week had been pure frustration. He'd been with his team tracking the storm across the eastern part of the state. But their search had been fruitless. One of the trucks had become lost on the back roads and they'd wasted more time when another had engine trouble. The only thing that had kept his temper at bay was the thought of seeing Dana again. And here he was stuck on a venture that was far from what he had in mind.

Too late now. He'd agreed to go. He decided not to worry about it and pitched in to help push the wobbly glider onto the runway. Dana showed him how to clip the cable connected to Kevin's plane.

"He'll pull us up until we find a thermal," she explained. "Then we'll release it and fly."

Her eyes glowed with excitement. Hal shook his head. He would never have believed that the woman he'd met—trembling and afraid of tornadoes—would be thrilled about climbing the circular currents of air in a glider. Dana was full of surprises.

Serious misgivings began to plague him though when he sat in the front seat ready for take-off. The glider tilted on a single wheel while its left wing rested on the ground. He peered through the bubble of Plexiglass. It didn't seem like there was enough to the craft to hold them up in the air.

Controls moved in front of him and he saw that Dana was checking the flaps. He turned around to see her working the struts. Her face was set and an air of expectancy hovered.

"Have you done a lot of this?" He wanted reassurance.

"Georgina and I used to come up all the time." She didn't look at him, but watched the flaps on the wing swing back and forth. "It's been fun since I've been back in Clear Creek because I don't get much of a chance to do this in L.A."

"Great," he muttered to himself and wondered if he shouldn't just climb out.

"I can't believe George hasn't taken you up."

Hal didn't respond. It wasn't that he hadn't had the opportunity. The glider flights were one of the town's main attractions. But he wasn't about to tell her he hadn't gone because the thought of it made his palms sweat.

"Do you see that knob?" Dana leaned forward, her breath feathering his neck. "When I tell you—pull it. It'll release the cable."

He nodded and gripped the edges of his seat. Kevin moved his plane slowly until the cable became taut. His engines revved. The glider wobbled its long wings like a wounded bird and then it left the ground.

Hal fought down panic as the craft took dives and jerks behind the plane. Higher and higher they rose until the fields below looked like a patchwork quilt and houses became tiny dots.

The scenery was breathtaking, but Hal barely noticed. His eyes were glued to Kevin's plane as it tugged against the strain of pulling the extra weight. The glider tossed about in its wake, making his stomach feel as if it'd dropped to his toes. Surely they would nosedive any minute.

Sweat beaded on his brow and trickled down his jaw. He wanted out. But they were committed now. There was no going back.

"We should hit a thermal anytime," Dana hollered above the rush of wind.

He wanted to close his eyes, but he didn't. Instead he concentrated on the confidence in her voice. Suddenly the glider lifted. His stomach lurched.

"Pull," Dana shouted.

For a split second he hesitated. He took a deep breath and grabbed the knob. He yanked. The clasp snapped and Dana banked the glider to the left. It circled higher and higher as if they were climbing a stairwell. Kevin's plane disappeared from sight and then it was quiet and smooth.

"Isn't this fantastic?"

He heard the enthusiasm in her voice and tried to focus on her words. Fantastic? Exciting? Daring? *Yes.* The challenge began to call. The familiar thrill of adventure charged through him and he smiled for the first time since they'd left the ground.

He called over his shoulder. "Dana Jean Cunningham. You're one gutsy lady."

HAL'S PRAISE of her courage carried her in a cloud for days. For the first time she realized that just because she feared tornadoes didn't mean she was a coward. It pleased her that Hal knew it, too.

At first she'd thought he didn't really enjoy the flying. But when he asked her to take him up the next day, she'd been delighted. They had spent hours climbing invisible spirals and soaring over the prairie. And here it was another Tuesday—a week gone by—and they were on the airstrip again.

"Man, that was something else," Hal told her as he helped her push their glider to its parking pad. "I could've stayed up there forever."

"I'm beginning to think you're part eagle," Dana teased before she glanced up at Bob and Candy who were coming in for a landing. Above them, two other gliders circled in the evening sky waiting for clearance. "It was fun having the others along, wasn't it?"

"I didn't think they'd all be able to come."

"Mondays and Tuesdays are the town's unofficial days off, since most of their business comes on the weekends," Dana explained.

"I knew that, but they all decided at the last minute to do this."

Hal may have been surprised, but Dana wasn't. Since Hal had stayed in town all this past week, she'd made every effort to include her friends on all of the get-togethers she'd had with him. It was insurance against getting involved. And a good thing too. Every time she saw him her attraction grew.

Like right now. He stood silhouetted by the setting sun. the breeze tossed his hair and she longed to run her fingers through it.

She could invite him to her place, fix dinner with candlelight and soft music and...and what? Make love to a man she had no intention of caring for?

As if he'd heard her thoughts, he swung his gaze to hers. In his eyes she saw desire and hunger as demanding as her own. Her heartbeat raced. With each second that ticked by, she felt herself drawn to temptation.

"Let's be alone tonight." His voice sounded husky with longing. "Just you and me."

Dana took a step toward him and stopped. Her mind struggled for reason while her body ached for his touch.

She finally managed to speak. "We said we'd go with them to Woody's. They'd be disappointed if we backed out on them."

"They'd understand."

She knew he was right. In fact her friends would cheer her on. At least all of them but Kevin. Even the young sheriff was beginning to realize there weren't the same sparks for him as seemed to fly around Hal. Dana closed her eyes. It would be so easy to give in.

"We promised, Hal," she reminded him and tried to be proud of her resistance.

He let out the breath he was holding. "Okay, golden girl. We'll have it your way tonight." He came to her then and draped his arm around her shoulder. With his free hand he tilted her face up to his and kissed her. It was a gentle kiss, but she knew from the strain in his embrace that he wanted more. And so did she.

All through dinner she tried to convince herself that she'd done the right thing. By the time she finished her steak and mushrooms, she began to believe it. Being at Woody's Woodshed helped.

The rustic restaurant and bar was the local hangout. The place was filled with deer antlers, Western antiques and stuffed jack-a-lopes, the latter of course, being the cause for jokes on the tourists. An ornate mirror behind the carved bar reflected jars of pickled eggs and beer nuts. Dana sat under one of the wagon wheels that hung from the ceiling, trying to get caught up in her friends teasing and joking.

"You should've heard Candy scream when we dropped into that cloud," Bob chuckled. "I thought she was going to split the canopy."

Candy waved her steak knife in mock threat. "You did that on purpose Bob Bradshaw. You get a perverted pleasure out of scaring me to death."

"You love it and you know it." Ben, her brother-in-law, reminded her.

"We girls aren't daredevils like you guys are." Susie came to her sister's defense.

"Except for Dana here." Kevin reached beside him and lifted Dana's hand in the air as if she were a champion. "We could never keep up with her."

"Come off it." Dana pulled her hand away. "I keep trying to tell you—I've changed."

"Huh," Kevin scoffed. "We saw you climbing over twelve thousand feet. You soared higher than any of us today."

She glanced to the other side of her at Hal. His eyes danced merrily. He hadn't believed she would go higher, and she had accepted the challenge. The others didn't need to know that. She merely shrugged. "It's too bad you can't catch those thermals."

Everyone booed.

"You're as bad as Underwood here." Bob smacked Hal on the back. "Always chasing after the wind."

A funny look came across Hal's face as he leaned toward her. "I think you need rescuing. Come dance with me."

She followed him to the corner of the rustic restaurant where Woody had set aside a dance floor by the old juke box. The lights were dim which helped give an air of intimacy.

"Pick something slow. I'm too stuffed to dance fast."

"My pleasure," he drawled as he wrapped an arm around her waist and pulled her close to his side.

She leaned her head against his shoulder and they looked over the selection of Western music. A warm easy feeling crept over her when a sexy number began to play.

"At last," Hal whispered in her ear after swinging her into his arms. "This is where I've wanted you all day."

His skin was hot beneath the sport shirt and she could smell the malty scent of his beer. She didn't mind being right where she was, but she wouldn't tell him that. Instead she said, "It would've been awkward flying in this position."

He paused for a moment and then gave her a slight squeeze. "Might've been interesting to try."

"You mean join the mile high club?"

"We both like challenges."

She chuckled as she tried to picture such activity in the cramped space of a glider. "I think I'm better off back there." She nodded toward the table. "You're giving me a worse time than they are."

"You're staying here." He drew her a shade closer. "Where I can have you all to myself."

"Not for long," she warned. "Here come Candy and Bob."

He spun her around to the far corner giving the other couple room on the floor. Before the song was over, several others had joined in. From then on the dancing continued until they closed the bar. But before that happened, the crowd got bigger and rowdier leaving no more opportunities for intimate moments.

IT TOOK MORE EFFORT than she was prepared for to get up the next morning and start working. "I'm not as young as I used to be," she muttered to herself as she tried again to concentrate on the list for the cleaning crew. Her ears still ached from the loud music and a few muscles she'd forgotten about were stiff. Was Hal as sore? The rat. He could sleep in.

"Morning, sunshine."

Speak of the devil, she thought.

He bounded through the door bursting with energy and looking handsome in slacks and a red polo shirt.

Dana groaned. Was he for real?

"What's the matter? Stay out too late last night?"

"Something like that." She tried to muster a show of enthusiasm. "What do you have planned?" She hoped he wanted to go fishing or something that would take him away. Her defenses were down.

"How about planning for your next days off?"

"That's a whole week away."

"Nothing like being prepared."

What was he up to? He sounded too casual. "More soaring?" she asked.

"It's a good time, but not what I had in mind." He crossed the lobby and braced his elbows on the registration desk. "I want to have you to myself for a change."

She started to protest, but he held up his hand.

"Come on, Dana. No friends, no parties—just you and me."

"It won't do any good. We only have time to be friends."

He shook his head with mock dismay and reached across the counter to grasp her fingers. "You can go on believing that if you want, but I know different."

She looked into the velvet brown of his eyes and almost agreed. He had a power over her that was becoming harder and harder to fight. Maybe she shouldn't bother anymore.

"What is it you'd like to do then?"

His fingers tightened around hers and she couldn't help but notice the relief in his gaze. "Would you like to come to the city and see the sights? We could tour the university and I'd show you the labs where I work."

The thought of two days at his house and in his working environment piqued her interest. But no, she stiffened her resolve. She'd spend time alone with him, but she wasn't going to give in to more than friendship.

"I'm enjoying being away from the rat race of the city. I'd rather stay here."

Her refusal didn't discourage him in the least. "Like to fish?"

"We could try that," she conceded.

"And a picnic?"

"Sounds fun."

"Camping?" he pushed.

"Just the day." She placed her hands on her hips.

"Okay." He laughed. "You've got a deal."

They chatted about the local fishing spots until guests claimed her attention. All morning he popped in and out of the lodge, and whenever she was free they discussed everything from their favorite foods, music and books to bets on who would win the baseball game playing next week.

Dana realized that the casual yet private chats were drawing her deeper into a relationship with Hal. The fact that they shared common interests, plus his easy-going manner, made it difficult to resist his charm.

By midweek she stopped trying. After all, what harm could come of a casual date or two? He didn't pressure her nor make any moves towards intimacy. Dana couldn't decide if she was relieved or disappointed about that. A part of her wanted to reach for the closeness they could share.

Thursday morning she decided to give in and at least invite him to dinner. From there, she didn't know what would happen. Maybe she'd let things go farther, but probably not. She had a feeling that if she went father than kisses with Hal, it would take her past a point of no return.

It took all morning for her to build up her courage to ask him over. By the time she figured she could, she realized she hadn't seen him. Strange. Where had he gone off to? Probably fishing, she guessed, when she saw the van was gone.

By noon her nerves were on edge as she cursed the appeal of fishing. She imagined he must be lazing away, pole dangling from his lap. Restless and needing action, Dana called Harvey to watch the lobby and drove her uncle's station wagon to the post office and then to the drug store to see Harriet.

"How's your arm?" she asked the older woman as she inspected her wound. It looked sore, but seemed to be healing.

"Coming along, missy. How you been?" Harriet greeted her. "Been seeing a lot o' the professor I hear."

"He's just overfriendly, Harriet. I couldn't very well kick him out of the lodge, now could I?"

Harriet chuckled and Dana relaxed. "I've got eyes and ears, missy. I heard how you two've been carrying on."

She remembered Sharon's earlier outbursts and wondered if Harriet objected. After all, she was Tommy's aunt. "Do you mind?" she asked the older woman.

"Land sakes, why would I mind a thing like that? It does my heart good to see a sparkle in your eyes."

Dana considered Harriet's observation. Yes, she sparkled and it felt good.

"You haven't seen Hal this morning have you? I wanted to ask him something."

"Didn't you hear the weather reports?" Harriet chided.

"No. What's the forecast?"

"A thunderstorm's brewing south of us."

"What does that have to do with Hal?" Suddenly she wanted him near. His strength would give her courage.

"He'd have to get back to the storm lab and get together his team. You know that."

His team? Suddenly she thought of the equipment in the back of the van. For gathering weather data, he'd said. And remarks made by her friends came to mind—comments about riding around in storms and chasing after the wind. Jokes, he'd said. The picture was becoming clear and Dana suddenly felt like ice.

"I don't know what you're talking about, Harriet. What team?"

"Nobody told you?" She stared at Dana, and understanding began to dawn in her eyes. So did pity. "I guess we thought you knew."

Dana managed to speak through her clenched teeth. "What team, Harriet? Why is he gone?"

"He's a storm chaser."

Panic surged into her system as a new meaning of the word hit her. "You don't mean he's one of those men who chase after tornadoes?"

"That's right, missy. He's gone after that storm."

6

A STORM CHASER! She couldn't believe it. She'd heard about the team of daring scientists, but never in her wildest imaginings had she figured Hal to be one. Of course when she stopped to think, it fit. With his sense of adventure and restless spirit, he would love the excitement of chasing after a dangerous tornado.

For what seemed like the hundredth time, Dana closed her mind to the thought. She refused to think about the rain, the lightning, the screaming wind...and Hal in the middle of it.

Why? She wanted to shout and beat her fists against his chest. Why hadn't he told her? She could have fought his charm easily if she'd known. She would never have allowed him near.

Her mind reeled with protest as she drove at breakneck speed back to the lodge. She should have been worried about the incoming storm, but all she could think of was Hal. Thank goodness she'd found out before she'd invited him to dinner. How would she feel if she'd let herself care for him and then had to send him off in a storm? Too late. She knew. The night promised to be full of worry as well as fear.

SIZZLING BACON filled the coffee shop with its delicious aroma, but Dana barely noticed. Her plate of eggs and hash browns remained untouched as she fingered her coffee cup. It had been a long night and she was exhausted.

Kevin, sitting across from her, looked rested and full of energy. His fresh appearance, however, didn't cover up his nervous tension. Dana sensed he had something on his mind.

"Thanks for checking on me during the night. You're a special friend," she told him. His arrival last evening had been welcome. The storm hadn't been as fierce as before, but his presence off and on had reassured her.

"I knew you needed me." He reached across and covered her hand with his. "I like being special, but I wish it was more than friendship."

"Kevin." His name echoed in half wail, half sigh. She'd always accepted his friendship over the years, never realizing he felt more than a sense of responsibility for his best friend's widow.

"Don't say anything." He held up his free hand. "I'd hoped that by coming back home, you might decide to stay and, well . . ."

"I can't stay here." Even if she could learn to live in Oklahoma again, her attraction to Hal ruined any hope for Kevin.

"I see that now. The storms . . ."

Dana turned her palm upward and squeezed Kevin's fingers. "You'll always have a special place in my heart, but—"

"It's not meant to be," he finished for her.

She shook her head and willed him to understand. Part of her regretted the truth. Kevin would be a caring husband and she longed for someone to love.

Uncomfortable with her thoughts, she tried to finish her breakfast. The eggs had no flavor and the toast crunched dry in her mouth. Just as she finished her last bite, the door to the small café jangled open.

Hal strode in, bringing an aura of raw power that reminded her of the storm he'd been chasing. He paused when he caught sight of her and stared. Lines of fatigue etched his features, but his eyes were bright and penetrating.

Dana's heart skipped a beat while a lump settled in her midsection. All the hours of worry came back to her. Had he found a tornado to place himself in front of? No. He stood there, healthy and energetic in spite of his being up all hours. As he approached their table, every part of her being screamed with awareness.

"Morning." He nodded to Kevin but kept his gaze locked with Dana's. "I was worried about you. Did you make it through the storm okay?"

"Kevin kept an eye on me."

His eyes narrowed and Dana felt the tension radiate from him. "I wanted to stay, but I had to go."

And chase a damn storm, she thought, as anger took control of her emotions. A lump formed in her throat making it impossible to speak. Trying not to let him see she had worried, she focused on Kevin. He was handsome, strong and her friend. Why hadn't she responded to him instead of to a storm chaser?

"The main front bypassed us," Kevin explained to Hal. "It stayed pretty quiet for the rest of the night. Did you see any tornadoes?"

In spite of her resolve not to look at him, Dana's glance flew to Hal.

"We confirmed some hook echoes in the supercells," Hal explained. "But they were weak and didn't touch down."

Dana listened to the technical explanation and reminded herself that she didn't want to care.

An uncomfortable silence settled over the threesome as Hal clearly waited for an invitation to join them. Dana bit her lip and Kevin frowned.

"Need a ride back to the lodge?" Hal broke the silence with his deep drawl. "I'm headed that way and could save you the trip, Sheriff."

"No." Dana quickly spoke up. "Kevin and I aren't ready yet."

Kevin looked relieved, but when Hal's jaw tightened, she knew he was upset. Dana tried to ignore the reactions of both men as she grabbed her coffee cup to steady her fingers. She wrapped her hand around the mug and tried to concentrate on its warmth.

When Hal left the café, Dana felt like a suffocating cloud had left with him. She sipped her coffee with an unsteady grip on the mug and cursed her reaction to Hal Underwood. Why did his presence send her world topsy-turvy? Why did he haunt her thoughts day and night? Why had she met a man like him now . . . a man with such a terrifying occupation?

"Dana Jean," Kevin reached over and touched her arm, bringing her attention back to him. "It's Underwood. You care a lot for him, don't you?"

"No," she lied and gave herself an inward shake. "I'm just tired."

"I understand. We're still going to be friends, aren't we?"

"Of course." Relief replaced her earlier tension. "How about stopping by for dinner tonight before you go back on duty?"

"Sure thing." Kevin smiled with genuine pleasure. "Always told Tommy he got the best cook in town."

A strange expression of remorse crossed his features as he realized what he'd said. With quick reflex, Dana reached out her hand to cover his.

"It's all right, Kevin. I like to talk about Tommy and remember those days." And strangely enough, it no longer hurt. "You were good friends, so it's natural to think about him."

"I don't want to hurt you."

"You won't." It was Hal who could hurt her, not Kevin.

Kevin spoke in his quiet, easy manner. "You're young, Dana Jean, and a real looker. A man'd be crazy not to be interested in you." They both knew he spoke of Hal as well as himself.

"We'd better go," was all she said.

Morning sunshine lifted over the horizon and warmed the chill from last night's storm. The bright rays felt good on her skin. To the west a rainbow arced color across the sky. An old melody came to mind and

Dana sighed. Did a new love wait somewhere over the rainbow for her?

HAL GUNNED THE MOTOR and entered the driveway of the lodge. He pulled up in front of his cabin, parked the van and began drumming his fingers upon the steering wheel. What had happened while he was gone?

Somehow, during the night, he'd lost what little headway he'd made with Dana. She had sat there and pretended to be interested in Kevin Blake. But she wasn't, he knew it. The real problem had to be something else. And he could guess what that was.

He slammed his fist on the steering wheel and vowed to make her understand. He would tell her about the storm chasing and make her see the importance of his work.

He stepped out of the van and paused while he watched the patrol car pull up in front of the lobby. She was golden sunshine in bright pink as she stepped out of the car. Hal caught his breath at the sight of her. Kevin Blake drove out of the yard and Hal debated. Should he go talk to her now?

He rubbed his fingers across the rough stubble of day-old beard and sighed as exhaustion took hold. No, he needed to be sharp and alert. A nap first, followed by a shower and shave and then, Dana Cunningham, watch out. He smiled as he strode into cabin twenty of Walkers' Lodge.

"YOU LOOK RESTED," Dana greeted him in the lobby later that morning.

She smiled, but Hal noticed the flicker of uneasiness in her eyes. Good, he still affected her. His confidence rose several notches.

"You look like you could use a break," he told her.

She looked fine actually, cheery in a red dress with puffy sleeves. Her hair flounced in a riot of natural curls, the ash-blond streaked golden by the sun. "How about joining me for a glass of iced tea?"

Her eyes flickered with indecision. Before she could say no, Hal came around the counter and grasped her hand. While he led her into the Walkers' private quarters, he relished her softness against the callused roughness of his fingers.

"Are you always so bossy?" she asked as she reluctantly followed him into the kitchen.

"'Course, didn't you know all professors get authoritative?" He cast her a devilish smile. "Comes from standing in front of a lecture hall telling all those people what to do and seeing them do it."

Her mouth quirked as she tried not to smile. Hal congratulated himself while he helped her pour tea. She looked lovely standing in the splash of sunlight. He wanted to pull her into his arms and taste her, caress her lips—caution. He pulled his thoughts up short and contented himself with smelling her light perfume and seeing the amber glints in her eyes.

"So tell me." There was too much casualness in her tone. "Do you prefer teaching or storm chasing?"

Hal tensed as he sucked in his breath. So she knew. He sat her in a chair and took the one across from it.

"I enjoy *all* of my work." He spoke carefully and sincerely.

Her eyes darkened until they were almost green. He had realized his work would upset her, but he was determined now to bring it out in the open and discuss it. She had to know what it meant to him.

"My research is important to me. The data we collect can help us give more accurate warnings."

She didn't say a word, but stared at him with eyes big and round.

"I need that sense of purpose and accomplishment. Imagine, Dana, how I feel when the warnings we issue save hundreds of people."

"Tornado warnings don't always save lives. Look what happened here at Clear Creek." Her voice rang with bitterness, and he thought he understood the reason for some of her mistrust in his work.

"That's exactly why our research *is* so important." In his excitement he reached across the table and clasped her hands in his. "Twelve years ago our predictions weren't that accurate. They still aren't. We can only predict that the weather conditions are right for tornado activity, so we issue the warning. But it's only a guess."

Restless and frustrated, he let go of Dana's fingers and began pacing the room. He missed the look of longing in her eyes as she followed his movements.

"People ignore the warnings because many times nothing comes of them." He rubbed the back of his neck to ease the tightness growing there. "That's why we need to gather the data from the actual tornado activity. If we can see how it looks on radar, our predictions will be better. In fact they already are."

"But what about your life?" Her voice rang with anguish. "Doesn't your life mean anything to you? You can't conduct research if you're blown away."

Hal stared at the concern in her eyes. Her objections were based on worry about his welfare and it touched him. It gave him hope for them.

"We're a team of scientists. We know what we're doing."

Their major danger, in fact, was not tornado activity but the threat of being struck by lightning while assembling their equipment. He didn't tell her that.

"For years our teams have been tracking storms. We don't actually see many tornadoes. We're lucky if we see five to nine each season."

"Knowing that doesn't help," she interrupted him, a tightness in her voice. "I worried all last night."

"Why did you worry?" He searched her expression for the truth. "Because you care for me?"

"Of course I care," she shot back, anger now in her tone. "I wouldn't want to see anyone hurt."

"Especially me?" he pushed.

Dana shifted in her chair and Hal moved with lightning speed to stand beside her. She turned to face him and he leaned down, almost touching her.

"We care for each other. Admit it, Dana. We have too much going for us to let it fall apart because you're afraid." He stared deep into her eyes, willing her to believe him. "We can work this out. I know we can."

"I don't want to work it out," she insisted with a stubborn set to her jaw. "I'll return to California where I won't have to face this."

"You won't run away. I know you won't." He was not sure of any such thing. He didn't want to lose her and he would fight with every advantage he had. "You won't hide behind Kevin Blake, either. He's nothing to you."

Her gasp of outrage alerted him to the fact that he had hit right on target. He hated pushing her this way. It would've been better to slowly win her trust and her love, but he didn't have the time.

"Kevin's my friend," she ground out between clenched teeth. Her temper matched his.

"Exactly." He remained bent over her, fighting the urge to claim her with a fierce kiss. "Be sure he knows that, too."

THAT EVENING, dinner with Kevin proceeded on a casual level. In spite of hating to be told what to do, Dana heeded Hal's advice. Not because he had given it, though, she insisted to herself, but because her honest nature wouldn't allow her to use a friendship in that manner.

Most of the evening they spent reminiscing about Tommy. Talking about her former husband did her a world of good. Over the years she'd idealized their relationship and put Tommy on a pedestal that would be hard for any man to step onto. Remembering the real Tommy helped put her memories in perspective.

For this purpose, her return to Clear Creek proved beneficial. Her memories would no longer prevent her from seeking another love. Because of that letting go, fighting off her attraction to Hal became more difficult.

As usual Hal came every day to visit with her while she managed the lodge. Fortunately the sunny weekend brought customers and dealing with them kept her occupied. But not enough to prevent her thoughts from turning to Hal during each idle moment.

Why did she find it so easy to keep her relationship with Kevin on a friendly basis but impossible to do the same thing with Hal? It annoyed her to always find him slipping into her thoughts.

The worst part of it was she couldn't hide her feelings from him. Every time Hal approached, her skin flushed, her heart pounded against her ribs and her breathing changed. But in spite of these clues to her feelings, she refused to permit anything to come of it.

On Monday morning, after the last guest checked out of the lodge, Dana spent an hour getting set up for Harvey to take over. There were still six rooms filled so she needed to be sure everything was in order. The books were already posted so all she really had to do was get the cleaning crew scheduled and started.

That accomplished, Dana faced the day with dread. Her day off and nothing to keep her from thinking about Hal. Idly, she wondered what Candy was doing, but decided to avoid her friend. Candy would only want to talk about Hal.

The front door opened and Dana looked up. Hal walked in, looking cheerful and smelling of the outdoors.

"Hello, sunshine." His greeting sent her heartbeat skittering. "Ready to go?"

"Go where?" Dana looked confused and wary.

"Fishing." He leaned over the counter and traced the line of her cheek with his finger. "You promised me, remember?"

Alarmed, she pulled back. She couldn't spend the day alone with this man. It would be too dangerous. But already, she longed to place her hand in his and follow.

"I don't think it's a good idea." The calm assurance in her voice relieved her.

"'Course it is." He cast her an irresistible smile. Dana wanted to trace the crease it made in his cheek. "Weather's perfect, no storms. What can go wrong?"

I could fall in love with you. The thought shook her. She closed her eyes and willed herself to remain calm and aloof.

"Dana." He came around the counter and placed his hands on her shoulders. Her eyes flew open and his tender look hypnotized her. "Have I made any demands on you?"

"No." She shook her head.

"You'll be safe with me. I won't ask anything that you don't want to give."

That was the problem. She wanted him to kiss her, the way he had before. She longed for his passion. She yearned for his promise of love and life.

This confusion disturbed her. She looked into the velvet of his eyes and pleaded for . . . what?—mercy or love?

"Dana." His breath caught in his throat and she could read the desire that matched hers.

Before reason took control, she lifted her lips to him. His kiss melted her resolve. The tension in his body relaxed as he gathered her into his arms.

"Come with me," he whispered against her neck, causing a momentary shiver.

Suddenly she wanted to go, wherever he led, whatever the cost. Her nod brought a smile to his face and happiness danced in his eyes. Dana's own heart soared as joy began to flow into the cracks of her heart.

"Let's go then," he urged as his mood lightened. "Those fish won't wait forever."

In the mad scramble that followed, Dana didn't allow herself to think of consequences. Her mind raced with the thoughts of what to wear, what to fix in their picnic and what to take. It didn't help when Hal teased her with challenges of who would catch more fish while he tried to sneak extra homemade cookies into the picnic basket.

Finally they made it to the lake loaded with crackers, cheeses, fruit, wine and, of course, cookies. Dana helped carry the gear from the van to the boat that was docked at the small local marina. She stood in gathered white cotton shorts and a bright baggy shirt splashed with yellows, blues and reds, and admired the small motor boat. The swivel seats and flat floor were ideal for fishing.

Hal filled the bait tank and fiddled with the engine while she arranged their belongings. Sunlight reflected on his tanned torso while he worked stripped to the waist and with cutoffs molded to his hips. How could she maintain a cool friendly manner with all that masculinity in full view?

"What shall the prize be for the one who catches the most fish?" he called out after anchoring in a cove and setting up the poles.

"I don't know," Dana shrugged absently while baiting her hook. "Got any ideas?"

He paused until Dana finally looked up. His eyes were filled with desire so strong, it made her tremble.

"I've got several ideas." His voice traced like velvet along her spine, rich and full of dark promise.

She cursed her shaking fingers and tumbling insides as she pretended to concentrate on her pole. Think of something quick. "The person who catches the most fish cleans and cooks them."

He let loose with a hearty laugh. "What kind of incentive is that?"

She cast him a smug grin and replied, "I haven't fished in several years, so I'm covering my bases."

"I see." A devilish gleam flickered in his eyes. "And does that mean the loser helps eat 'em?"

She realized his trap too late. She hadn't agreed to spend the evening with him. Now it seemed as if she'd talked herself into a commitment. The waters of temptation were getting deeper.

Evidently content with his victory, he didn't make any further advances. The gentle lapping of water on the hull of the boat and the warmth of the sun soon relaxed her. Several other fishing boats drifted off far shores, but none came near to disturb their peace. The occasional flutter of a breeze ruffled her shoulder-length hair. All of her tensions melted away in the peaceful silence.

"I wish every day was sunny and tranquil like this," she said dreamily. "I'd return to Clear Creek to stay."

"Why?"

His question floated across the water, tantalizing in its simplicity. Could she tell him all the reasons that called to her? Her childhood, her friends . . . him.

"Do you ever feel alone in the city?"

He shrugged and gazed at her with an unsettling intensity. "I'm alone, but not because I live in the city."

She understood what he meant, but made no effort to encourage him.

"Don't forget, I'm on campus most of the time. In many ways that's like a small community."

"I suppose." The picture of Hal on campus among stuffy highbrows amused her. She looked across the boat at his casual attire and relaxed manner. "It's hard to picture you dressed in a suit and giving lectures to a bunch of eager students."

"I don't wear suits." He wrinkled his nose. "We dress casually in the science wing."

That picture came easier than the last. He would look sexy dressed in a cashmere sweater and cords.

"I bet all the coeds have crushes on you."

"'Course." The crease in his cheek deepened with his smile. "I have to find places to hide or I can't get my work done."

He was teasing, but Dana found his statement believable.

"Just last semester, I got stuck after class for an hour. Two girls decided they needed a better description of how weather balloons function. I could tell neither one really cared, but I decided a lesson was what they asked for and a lesson they'd get. I took them outdoors with trial balloons . . ."

Interested, Dana listened. His voice drawled in the lazy afternoon heat. Funny stories spurred her imagination as she thought about him in the safe role of instructor.

"You make it sound exciting," she told him. "Your students must love your lectures."

"Most seem interested, but I'm tough."

"They respect that. I never admired wishy-washy instructors."

His laughter rang across the quiet waters of the lake, startling several ducks from nearby marsh rushes. "No. They wouldn't call me that."

Sudden images of his strength and daring brought to mind his other work. Of course, he needed to be tough and adventurous to search out tornadoes.

"Why isn't teaching enough for you?" She suddenly had to know.

She knew he understood her question, but he sat silent and observing for several moments. A breeze wafted by, tossing his chestnut hair across his forehead. The auburn tints glinted in the sunlight, but a shadow clouded his features.

"Do you want me to quit my research?" he asked her in a quiet voice. "Is that what would make you stay?"

It was tempting to beg him to give up the dangerous project. Perhaps she could learn to live through the storms. Perhaps she could remain in the Midwest. Perhaps she could experience life again in the safety of his arms.

But no, the image shattered with the reality of the man. In spite of the fact that he sat fishing, apparently calm, she sensed the inner restlessness that ran through him. He needed to meet the challenge of discovering nature's secrets. The dedication that drove him to save lives had salvaged his own. Giving up his research would destroy the man she admired.

"I could never ask you to do that," she told him and watched the cords of his neck relax. "I know what your work means to you."

"It's important."

"So is your life," she couldn't help but add.

In a flash of movement he set his pole into the holder and knelt before her. After propping her rod across the bow, he took her face between his long fingers and stared deep into her eyes willing her to believe. "I won't die on you, sunshine."

7

SMALL WAVES LAPPED against the hull, the sound mocking his words. "You can't make a statement like that," she told him, wishing with sudden intensity that he could.

He pulled her face toward him and leaned closer to brush her lips with his. "Believe it, Dana. I never make promises I don't keep."

Her lips tingled where his had been. He tasted male. Yes, she could almost believe his arrogance. But no man, especially one who challenged nature, could defy its laws.

But for a tempting moment, she pretended his words were true. Laughter and loving teased her imagination. What this man could give to her made her ache with inner longing. But that happiness could be snatched from her as quickly as before. No, she wouldn't seek that kind of pain.

Her eyes must have clouded with skepticism because Hal let her go and returned to his seat in the boat. With a covert glance, she focused on the relaxed pose he assumed. Feet stretched before him, arms raised and bent with his fingers entwined to brace his head, he appeared content.

"Aren't you wondering how I'm so certain?" he asked, a blandness to his drawl.

"Are you certain?" she countered, annoyed now by his nonsense.

"'Course." He smiled at her, and Dana had to will herself not to be pulled in by its warmth. "I can picture the future, you see."

Giving in to this ridiculous game, Dana leaned back in her own seat and closed her eyes. "See what?" she said with a tinge of exaggerated sweetness.

"You and me. Why it's as clear as a bell. Years from now, we'll be sitting here on the same lake, soaking up the sun and fishing, lazy and content."

Dana opened her eyes and stared in amazement. She wanted to believe him, and his confidence encouraged her to try.

"It wouldn't be the same." She smiled as the vision focused in her mind.

"'Course not. I'd be crotchety and wrinkled, but you'd still be the most beautiful woman around."

"Flattery isn't going to make me believe you." But his words did tug at the cords of her heart.

"I can see it so clearly," he mused. "It must be real."

"You're a dreamer."

"Don't you have hopes and dreams?"

His question disturbed the peace beginning to settle upon her. "I used to, but I know they aren't real. They're just illusions."

"You can learn again. Start now."

She wanted to pretend with him and believe his fantasies, but storm clouds darkened the skies whenever she thought of Hal. She couldn't afford to place her desires in his care, no matter how much she longed to.

A jerk on her fishing line created a thankful distraction. Her excitement was a bit overdone as she called attention to the biggest catch of the day.

"If this keeps up," she gloated, "I may have to cook and clean these guys."

"Don't count your fish before they hatch," he said changing the adage to suit his needs. "I still have the biggest count."

"Surely this one counts as two," she declared.

"No chance."

He grabbed the fish from her and proceeded to thread it on the stringer with the other silvery bass. They struggled, causing their scales to reflect in the sunlight. For a brief moment Dana felt remorse at capturing such wild beauty.

"Don't look like that," he chided her. "I'll have to set 'em all free."

"Would you?" she asked.

As if aware of a deeper intent to her request, he paused to consider his answer. Dana watched the emotions play across his face—reluctance, male pride—all mixed with the desire to please. "If you asked."

"It's a good thing I'm hungry then," she declared with mock indignation. "I refuse to let these babies go."

He laughed with her, but Dana enjoyed his relief.

"Don't let anyone else wrap you around their finger," she warned. "You're a real pushover."

"Better not have any daughters then."

Dana's heart thudded to a stop, to be followed by a longing so painful as to tear at her insides. A sudden image flashed of a little girl with doe-brown eyes and chestnut curls to match her father's.

"I'd think you'd want sons." She hoped he didn't notice the catch in her voice.

"I do want a boy." His voice held sincerity, but Dana could not bring herself to look into his eyes. "I want a son I can teach the wonders of life and what it is to be a man."

His words captured her and she glanced up to lock gazes.

"And a daughter?"

"I'd want one that looked just like her mother, with sun-gold hair and laughing eyes that change colors with her mood." Then he winked, lightening her spirit. "And so I could spoil her just like I would her mother."

"You mean so she'll spoil *you*." Dana decided to follow his lead and ease the tension.

He shrugged and amusement danced in his eyes. "Sounds like a good idea."

"You have it all planned, a son and daughter. Careful, professor, or you could scare a woman off with those kinds of demands."

"You've had a child. The prospect shouldn't frighten you." He spoke with careful regard.

"It's the fact that I have that does." She laughed with a rueful twist of humor. "Children are a handful. If Tommy and I'd known, we might've planned more carefully ourselves."

"You mean you wouldn't have had any?"

Memories softened her heart. "We would've had children, but we were just kids ourselves and didn't give any thought to the responsibilities. I think we both might have wished for more time to grow up."

Dana went on to relate different aspects of their youthful parenthood. Once the dam had opened, she released a flood of memories. Some of them were difficult, but now she could remember the humor in their inexperience. "We did some pretty foolish things now that I have the maturity to realize it."

"Maturity has its advantages," Hal commented.

Yes, Dana thought, and wisdom comes with it. "We just jumped into everything without much thought to consequences," she mused aloud.

"And that's the disadvantage of maturity." Hal reached over and brushed a wayward curl behind her ear. Dana looked up, startled by his touch.

"Why is that?" Did her voice sound breathless?

"Maturity makes you cautious. You won't jump into a relationship with me." A touch of chiding threaded through the regret in his tone. "You're too concerned with the consequences."

Dana searched his expression and saw the hint of anger. Her reluctance was unfair. She'd be the first to admit it. There were so many things that were right between them. But Dana had her fears and Hal had his research. No, caution was wise.

But when he sat so close, the heat from his sun-warmed skin reached her. His clean athletic scent enveloped them and his touch sent her reason flying. She clenched her fists and resisted the urge to reach out to him. A flush of desire darkened her cheeks.

"Forget being sensible and let me kiss you," he whispered.

Her pulse raced as he leaned closer. His breath tickled her lips before she could pull away. She met him halfway. When his lips met hers a moan tore from her throat. Longings rose up to drown all sense of reason. She wanted his kiss—she needed it.

Arms that she now felt at home in wrapped around her. She could feel the strength in his fingers as he searched out her sensitive places through the folds of her cotton blouse. His mouth made tender demands upon hers.

A tremor coursed through her body. She could feel the tautness in his muscles and sense the strain in his kiss. He wanted her, but he'd let her lead the way. Her heart turned over at that knowledge.

She smoothed her fingers across the hard muscles of his back and reveled in the satin feel of his skin. His chest felt solid as she pressed her curves against him. She wanted him, too.

"You're so sweet," he murmured, his breath heating her neck.

"Kiss me again," she begged.

"I need you, Dana. I can't tell you how much."

His hunger drove hers, but she heard the ache in his voice. She must stop torturing them both. She must forget her fears—for now. She pulled her lips away and took a deep breath. "I need you, too."

He froze. His voice sounded breathless. "Are you saying . . ."

"Let's go back to the lodge."

For seconds he didn't move. His arms remained locked around her and she thought he hadn't heard. She almost fell over when he did release her. Relief, joy and excitement flashed across his features. At that moment, Dana realized he hadn't been as sure of her as she supposed. The touch of vulnerability made it easier for her.

"We can be packed up and on our way in ten minutes," he promised.

"You'd better reel in your line." She nodded to his pole which was jerking in its holder for who knew how long.

He stared at the bent rod as if unable to focus, until realization dawned. He grabbed the rod. "You bring me luck." He flashed a mischievous grin over her shoulder.

Dana smiled back as she started to reel in her own line. Her fingers trembled but she managed to pack up her gear with surprising speed.

True to his word, Hal had them back at the marina in ten minutes. Dana scarcely remembered docking the boat, unloading their supplies or even driving the short distance back to the lodge. Hal moved with such speed she wondered if he was afraid she'd change her mind.

He needn't have worried. She doubted she could have changed the course of events even if she'd wanted to. And she didn't want to. She'd been honest when she'd told him she needed him.

He parked the van in front of his cabin and stared straight ahead. His hands gripped the steering wheel. Dana took a deep breath. Had he changed *his* mind?

His voice was strained when he spoke. "Now's the time, Dana, before we go inside. If you're going to have regrets...."

His words tore at her heart. She reached across the space and barely touched his lips. "I'll probably have regrets, storm chaser. We both will." She trailed her fingers along his jaw. "But I'm going to follow your advice and jump right in—for today anyway."

"And tomorrow?"

"I can't make any promises."

He looked at her then. His eyes blazed with passion and longing and his own brand of fear. "I'll take today."

Before she could say another word, he stepped out of the van and pulled her with him. He lifted her into his arms and slammed the door shut with his foot.

"The fish—"

"Are in the cooler," he assured her as he stepped onto the porch of his cabin. He twisted sideways to insert the key. The door opened and he stepped inside.

Her arms tightened around his neck as the silence and privacy enveloped them. The room was dark until her eyes adjusted from the outside glare. But she knew a king-size bed sat in the middle of the knotty pine room, and Hal went straight to it.

He let her slide down until her feet touched the braided rug on the floor. She could feel the taut readiness in his body. It made her weak with longing and she leaned against his strength.

"Love me," she begged with sweet demand.

A shudder tore through him as he molded her to his hardness. "I've wanted to hear you say that," he whispered. "I've wanted so badly to make love to you."

"Please." It was the only thing she could say.

All thoughts of consequences and all fears for their future vanished. Her sole purpose for the moment was to feel the sensations coursing through her. Hal stepped away and pulled back the comforter until it was draped across the foot of the bed.

He stood before her. With slow precision he unbuttoned his cutoffs. Dana's heart thumped against her chest as she reached shaky fingers to trace the line of hair to his navel. His stomach muscles tightened at her touch.

She flashed a wide-eyed glance to his face and saw his shaky smile. Her heart slowed a fraction until his hands reached for the waistband. She took deep, gulping breaths and watched in a trance as he slid his cutoffs to the floor.

Somewhere in the rational recesses of her mind she realized his purpose. He undressed first to make it more comfortable for her. Nakedness left a woman vulnerable. He understood. At that moment, her feelings for him deepened.

For several seconds, he stood stock still, warm air caressing his naked flesh. Her gaze traced the lines of his skin as she explored every rigid inch of his body.

Her fingers trembled as she tried to unfasten her own clothing. Hal stepped close and covered her hands to still their shaking. "Let me." His breath feathered the tendrils of hair at her temple.

Dana closed her eyes and enjoyed the currents of pleasure that jolted through her with each touch. By the time she stood naked, she felt fine-tuned and taut. Her breath came in gasps while her skin felt on fire.

"You're breathtaking," he murmured. His gaze burned. He reached out to touch and paused. "You're a rare piece of art."

She trembled with longing. "Touch me."

His warm hands closed over her shoulders and then slid down her back to pull her against his body. She felt the brush of his hairs, satin of his skin and the steel of his muscles. Her knees buckled. She wrapped her arms around his neck and clung to the sensations that were making her want to scream.

The contact sent sparks flying between them. Hal groaned. Dana fell toward the bed and he followed beside her.

"I wanted to go slow, to make this right." His hands traveled all over her body. "But so help me, Dana, I've got to have you now."

She knew. She couldn't wait either. They had wanted each other for too long. It didn't seem as if she could touch enough of him.

His arms pulled her tight against his body until her curves molded to his angles. Suddenly he released her and placed her on her back. Startled, she stared into his eyes. They burned into her with devouring need. He placed his hand on her thigh and with slow torture, opened her legs.

She stiffened as anticipation rocketed through her. He held her firm.

"It's all right," he promised. With a brush of his lips he smoothed back the damp tendrils of hair from her forehead.

"I know." She took deep panting breaths and waited for him.

Then suddenly he was there—above her and all around her. She clasped his heated body and pulled him close. His heart thundered in her ear. She dug her nails into his back, her fervor raging beyond control. "Love me now."

He positioned himself on top of her and paused. She could feel his throbbing heat ready to take possession. Her body strained for his fire. She arched her hips to his and heard her name echo in the room as he cried out in sweet agony.

Hal took giant gasps of air as he forced himself to wait and let her adjust to his presence inside of her. He knew he had found home. Never had a woman felt so right and so special. He wanted to take his time with her but his body demanded action. He groaned and began to move.

She matched his rhythm until they were both out of control. The muscles that sheathed him contracted and he held on tight. But her moans of pleasure sent shockwaves through his system and he exploded.

"Dana." Her name sang through his veins as he gave her all of himself.

Quiet settled over their damp bodies. Hal knew without doubt that he had never felt such satisfaction nor had he felt such overwhelming love. He rested his forehead against hers and closed his eyes as a final shudder drained his last ounce of energy.

Afraid he might be hurting her, he rolled onto his side and brought her against him. The wildflower scent of her hair mingled with the musk of their lovemaking. He breathed deeply and contentedly.

Sunlight danced across the knotty pine panels on the wall of the cabin. The patterns changed as the breeze filtered it through the curtains. Dana shifted onto her elbow. "This was a mistake." Her voice cut into the euphoria surrounding him.

He froze. Then after his heartbeat started up again he managed to speak. "Regrets already, sunshine?"

"Yes." She began tracing the line of his jaw, a winsome smile curving her mouth. "Now I know this will never be enough of you. I'm going to want more."

His stomach tensed against the fist that seemed to be slamming into it. She sounded as though she didn't believe there would be more. "You can have all of me you want."

"What a promise. Are you sure you know what you're committing yourself to?"

"I know what I'd like to commit myself to." He wanted the future but he knew it was too soon for that. He brushed back a tendril of hair from her cheek. "How about a whole night of you?"

She chuckled. "What about our fish dinner? Aren't you hungry?"

He grabbed her fingers and brought them to his mouth. He nipped at the soft flesh. "I'm hungry for you."

"Not very nourishing."

"But appetizing."

She ruffled his hair and laughed. "Harvey'll see the van and know we're here. I should go on over to my place."

He caught her wrists and rolled her onto her back, pinning them to her sides. "Are you running away? It won't do any good. I'll be right behind you."

Flickers of doubt and unease reflected in her eyes. He knew he shouldn't pressure her but he wanted so badly to talk about what had just happened between them. It had been special for him and he knew it had been for her, too. Her gaze pleaded for understanding.

He laughed and the tension fell away from both of them. Still holding her wrists, he nuzzled down to tickle her ribs with his chin. She squirmed from under him and jumped out of bed.

"Not fair." She laughed.

Sunbeams danced across her skin. He swallowed hard at the sight. "Neither are you," he groaned.

Dana chuckled and began to slip into her clothes. They didn't hide the fact she'd just come from his bed. Her hair was mussed and her skin was flushed. He couldn't tear his gaze away as he watched every move.

When she finished, she knelt on the edge of the bed and placed a light kiss on his lips. "Relax and take a nap or whatever." She kissed him again. He wanted to grab her and taste more but he enjoyed her spoiling him too much. "Come on over in an hour or so and we'll have dinner and . . ."

"And?" He trailed his finger up her bare thigh.

She shivered. "I'll take you up on your promise."

Breathless, he smiled and watched her leave. He'd promised her all of him but she'd only promised him today.

For long moments he lay there and willed his insides to stop tumbling. There was still time. It wouldn't do any good to rush her. After all he hadn't even thought of the future himself until this afternoon. He'd never considered remarriage since his bitter divorce. But the idea had slid into his thoughts with unexpected strength. While he was getting used to it himself, he could work on Dana's fears.

He swung his legs off the bed in a typical flurry of motion. Faced with a challenge, his usual approach was to attack it headlong. He quickly showered while he made his plans.

Thankfully he'd been around when the lodge was rebuilt. He'd use that knowledge and show Dana she didn't have to fear the storms. After she overcame those worries, he could work on convincing her to stay. He tucked his safari shirt into his khaki slacks and set off to find Harvey. With luck, he'd have everything ready before dinner. Time was running short.

An hour later he found her in the kitchen frying up the last of the fish. She'd showered and changed. As usual when he saw her, his heart knocked against his ribs while a knot formed in his midsection. The sight of her hit him harder since they'd made love.

When she saw him her face lit up and that encouraged him. The dimple at the side of her mouth flashed when she smiled. He loved it. He wanted to hold her close, but he resisted the urge.

Their dinner conversation was light. It took effort to talk about fishing and soaring when he wanted to discuss what had happened between them in the cabin that afternoon. Finally, it was over and he helped her clean up. After hanging up the dish towel, he went to her side.

"Come along." He held out his hand and prayed she'd take it without a fuss. "Harvey says he'll watch the office for a couple more hours. I have something I want to show you."

Her expression was filled with curiosity. He let himself enjoy the pleasure that ran through him when her fingers wrapped around his. A faint scent of wildflowers followed them down the hall.

When they arrived at the head of the stairs to the cellar, he felt Dana tense. He opened the door and a whoosh of dank air chilled the fingers that clenched his so tightly.

"Why're we going down there?" He could hear the apprehension in her voice.

"I want to prove to you that you're safe from storms." He gestured to the poured concrete storm cellar. She started to resist, but he pulled her with him down the stairs and around the ninety degree turn in the entranceway. "See. These sharp turns keep flying objects from coming inside the shelter. There aren't any windows, which is better than cellars that have them."

He flicked on the light and stepped around the rows of cots. There were enough for guests of the lodge, should they have an extended stay in the shelter. They rarely needed to supply protection for a full house. Most guests were weekenders from the city and if a storm was predicted, they didn't come to Clear Creek.

"The northeast corner is actually the safest part of the cellar, contrary to popular belief," he advised her. "If you're caught without a cellar, that's a good general rule to follow. Look for a closet or a small room in that part of the building."

Suddenly she interrupted him. "This is just fine." He turned to see that her eyes had darkened with bitterness. "But what if there's no tornado warning? You know, don't you, that the watch had been lifted the night the tornadoes hit Clear Creek?"

"That's true," he admitted, undaunted by her rancor. "But follow me and I'll show you why that won't be a problem anymore—at least not in Clear Creek."

He held her hand and led her out of the cellar. Hal guided her to the foot of the stairs to the attic and proceeded to mount them.

"Don't tell me you believe the old wive's tale that a tornado won't strike in the same place twice?"

"'Course not," he drawled as he led her up the stairs. "Nor does it matter that the probability of a tornado striking a given spot is only one in a few hundred years."

"That statistic doesn't help when one is roaring down on you," she agreed, the slight hint of ironic humor in her tone giving him confidence. "What on earth are we doing up here? It's dusty and full of spiders."

Hal turned to see her swatting at the dangling webs. The way her nose was scrunched up in distaste made him chuckle. "Scared?" he taunted.

"No." Her back stiffened and she tossed her head. "But I'm beginning to think you're nutty after all."

Hal's laughter echoed in the eerie shadows of rafters and eaves. One section of the attic had flooring, where George stored boxes of his belongings. Hal bypassed these and guided Dana to the edge where he stepped out onto a beam.

"Most damage occurs when the winds blow off a roof," he explained. "Because of cheap construction, the walls collapse when the roof flies off."

He peered at her to be sure she was listening with close attention and then continued to explain. "See those split ring connectors? And look, George even went to the expense of adding gusset-plate joints."

Her expression was endearing. It was a combination of confusion and attention. He wanted to smooth her furrowed brow, but went on to explain in more detail. "Before the tornado, the roofs were only nailed on. The force of the wind blew them off, causing the walls to collapse." He pointed to the connectors. "Those connectors hold the roof on."

She asked many questions and her growing enthusiasm eased some of the tension he'd felt earlier. His heart began to fill with relief. Perhaps she would understand that she was safe when buildings were constructed for severe storms. Maybe then she wouldn't be afraid.

"With these improvements, it's possible to construct homes that can withstand winds of up to two hundred miles an hour," he assured her. "This lodge and all the rebuilt homes in Clear Creek are now protected."

"Why didn't they build homes like that in the first place?" she asked, her eyes wide. Was there hurt in their depths; anger for the waste of property and lives? If so, he empathized with her.

"It's a sad fact, but most people assume a tornado will never happen to them...only to someone else." His own anger began to swell as his pet peeve surfaced. "Contractors cut costs by using lower grade materials and they don't put in the special struts and trusses. Why, they don't even build basements anymore."

"How do they get away with that?" she asked, her bitterness evident again.

"There aren't building codes strict enough, for one thing." He gestured in agitation with a wide swing of his arm. "But if people buy the houses without demanding proper protection, then they're perpetuating the problem."

"How would anyone know to demand such things?" Her face had turned ashen.

He realized he had become carried away with his tirade and relented. He tried to reassure her as he gathered her close with his arm across her shoulder.

"I'm sorry. I guess I get carried away on my soapbox." He cast a sheepish grin and hugged her to him. "But it's one of our major concerns—educating the public."

Hal didn't let her go. He wanted to savor the feel of her against him. But he was surprised when she turned in against his chest and wrapped her arms around his waist.

"It's such a waste, isn't it?" she murmured into his shirt. "So many lives lost, property damaged...I didn't realize how needless it all was."

He sensed emotions deeper than those she expressed and enfolded her tighter in his arms. He buried his face in her curls and let her feel his strength.

"You see why our work is so important?" he murmured, his lips brushing her temple as he rocked back and forth.

"I'm beginning to understand more and more." She sighed and pulled herself closer against him. "No wonder Candy said they aren't afraid anymore."

"They still have fear, but by and large proper protection eases much of the worry."

No response followed his statement, but he felt the tension still tightening her muscles. His own were beginning to stiffen, but from a different source. The soft curves pressing against the surfaces of his body sent messages racing at full alert. When she shifted slightly, he almost groaned with the ache surging through him.

The urge to pull her face up and kiss her became stronger, but he resisted. At the moment she sought solace. He wouldn't betray her trust.

Instead, he savored the soft pliancy of her flesh pressed to his. The wildflower perfume mixed with her personal scent feathered the air around them. He enjoyed her touch until she broke away.

The time spent in his arms had strengthened her composure. Good. If he just had months instead of weeks, he knew he could win her. At least he had tonight.

ANOTHER WEEK FLEW BY with surprising speed. Considering how much time she'd spent warding off her deepening feelings for Hal Underwood, Dana thought the time would drag. She'd even refused to make plans for her days off this week. Now she wished she had. Would she see him? She sighed. Thank goodness she only had a few days left or she feared she would find herself in love again.

As she stood behind the registration desk, she heard a car drive up. She hoped it was Hal, and that annoyed her. Quickly, she fluffed her curls and straightened her yellow sun dress. The door opened and Dana tried to hide her disappointment when she saw who it was.

"What's the matter, missy. Were you hoping for a customer?" Harriet paused and placed her finger across her lips in a thoughtful pose and then snapped her fingers as if she'd just remembered something important. "Of course, I bet it's the storm chaser you're expecting."

She sighed. Reminders of Hal's occupation sent shivers of unease down her spine.

"It's good to see you." Dana ignored Harriet's teasing and came from behind the counter to give the woman a hug. "Have some coffee with me. You're up early."

"Since it's your day off, me and the girls thought you might want to play some bridge this morning." Harriet accepted the cup of coffee Dana poured from the pot they kept there for guests. "'Course that's if you don't already have plans."

"I don't have any," she assured Harriet. Hal had tried to make plans but she'd insisted that she needed some time to herself. She was afraid if she spent her last days off with him, she'd give in and take what loving she could. It wasn't fair to Hal nor to herself. Neither of them would be satisfied with that.

She could tell Harriet was about to ask her why she wasn't with Hal, but luckily two cars pulled into the driveway and parked out front. Dana peered out the window and saw that the other women had arrived for bridge.

The bustle and chatter of their entrance put a stop to the conversation. Dana was relieved.

"We didn't hear from Harriet so we figured the game was on."

"Dana, you're my partner," Candy insisted.

"I'll get the card tables. I know where Lillian hides 'em."

By the time the tables were set and the cards dealt, Dana had a fresh pot of coffee perking and had taken some sweet rolls out of the freezer. Her spirits lifted and continued to climb with each trump card played. In a little more than an hour, she had completely joined in the friendly gossip and forgotten about Hal.

"You should see Woody's new waitress. Is she a looker."

"I better keep an eye on Bob next time we go there then."

"You know he's crazy in love with you. He'd never look at another woman."

"He better not," Candy threatened with mock severity before she made another bid.

Harriet played a card and asked, "Has Sharon returned from Hawaii yet?"

Dana stiffened. She hoped Jim and Sharon wouldn't get back until after she'd left. It had been easier for her to get around town without having to worry about meeting up with them."

"She's going to be gone two more weeks, the lucky." Suzy sighed with envy.

"I'd sure like to go there. Have you been, Dana?"

"No, I haven't taken many vacations."

"It's a good thing," Harriet told them, "or she wouldn't have been able to come here."

Was it a good thing? At times like this she thought so. But then . . . Before she could think about it anymore the conversation got around to Georgina and the baby and the Walkers' trip to Florida.

"Georgina must love living on the beach. Remember—"

A knock sounded on the door. Dana looked up to see Hal come around the corner.

"Morning, sunshine."

The room grew still. Dana knew she should say something but her throat tied up at the sight of him. His yellow plaid shirt gave his skin a warm glow. She wanted to be caught up against it, she wanted to hold him.

Harriet finally broke the spell with her usual no nonsense. "Morning, professor. If you want Dana, you'll have to wait until she finishes this round."

Several chuckles eased the tension, but Dana noticed the women still eyed him with interest. She couldn't blame them. He did command one's attention with all that raw virility.

"Don't worry," Candy assured him. "We're winning and in for a kill. This'll be over in a flash."

"Good." He smiled, not bothering to politely tell them to take their time. "We have to get going."

Dana stiffened in surprise. What nerve to barge in on their game like this. "I'll have Harvey let you know when we're done." She tried to politely dismiss him.

"I'll wait." He oozed charm, but Dana heard the ring of determination.

"Where you off to in such an all-fired rush?"

Leave it to Harriet to ask. Didn't they know it was just a ruse to get them to leave? He wanted her to himself, but she wasn't going to let him get away with that. She started to explain they weren't going anywhere when his words stopped her cold.

"I'm taking Dana to Oklahoma City."

Her cards fell to the floor.

Candy jumped up. "Dana, you're showing your hand."

"Good heavens," Harriet waved Candy back in her chair. "What difference does it make? Can't you see she's too flustered to finish this game anyway."

Several giggles followed that remark. Dana came to her senses.

"I'm not going to the city." She didn't like embarrassing him with her refusal in front of the others, but he was calling the shots.

He didn't bat an eye but came over to her table and hunkered down. "Let's bet on it. Blackjack. Harriet, your deal." He collected Dana's cards from the floor while the older woman swooped up those on the table.

Suddenly the room was full of commotion as everyone gathered round. The uncomfortable feeling that she was being railroaded crept over her and she started once again to protest. Before she uttered a word, Harriet dealt the cards.

"Turn 'em, missy."

Dana hesitated. She should refuse and order him out of the room for pulling such a high-handed stunt. But the challenge was out. She couldn't resist. She flipped the cards.

A queen of hearts and a king.

The women groaned, making it obvious whose side they were on. Triumph gave her confidence. She gave him a saucy grin and dared him to look at his hand.

With slow deliberation, he fingered the corners of the cards. The suspense thickened as everyone held their breath.

"Turn them." Her voice was low and confident.

He drew one card. The king of hearts. Slowly he lifted the other and held it out to her. She gulped and looked again to be sure. The ace of spades.

8

THEY WERE on the outskirts of Oklahoma City and Dana still wondered if it was a good idea to come with Hal. She was courting heartache. She knew it, but couldn't seem to stop herself.

From under her thick lashes she stole covert glances as he drove the van through the traffic. The muscles in his arms flexed with each shift of gears. His slacks stretched taut over the columns of his thighs before they loosened below the knee to drape the rest of his legs. It took no imagination to remember the feel of those limbs.

Uncomfortable with the trend of her thoughts, Dana shifted in her seat. The new position only brought him into better view. Now she could see his chest. How many times had she lain her head there? Or what about the times she'd placed her cheek into the curve of his neck? Her pulse quickened. Would they make love this afternoon at his place?

She forced her gaze upward and concentrated on his profile. It was rugged and angled with strong features. Dana could imagine him racing across the stormy prairies with excitement glittering in his dark brown eyes. He looked the adventurer. She could see him dressed in buckskins, an explorer in earlier days. That sense of restlessness would drive him to map out new regions and discover new frontiers.

His strength called to her. It was too easy to picture herself at his side, giving him support and love. A small moan escaped her lips.

"We're almost there." Her eyes flew to his. Had he heard her moan and, worse, could he guess the reason for her distress? She avoided his gaze and peered at the green fields they were passing through.

"Your house is out here?" she asked in surprise.

"The Severe Storms Lab is near here." He cast her a sideways glance and a crooked smile. "I'm taking you on a tour."

"You never give up do you?" Her fingers tightened into fists as she fought to control the nervousness and resentment.

"Not where you're concerned." His tone became serious. "I'm going to prove to you that you're safe here."

"It's not just *my* safety I'm concerned about." She wanted to scream, but she sounded calm enough. "It's yours."

"You're going to see how well trained we are. Then you'll see that I'm not in any danger."

"How can you say that? Placing yourself in front of a tornado is a death wish."

"Only an average of ninety-three people die from tornadoes every year and mostly because they weren't warned or didn't know what to do."

"That's not the point. It's that I'd know you were out there chasing the damned things."

"Come on, Dana. You're exaggerating."

Dana refused to respond and kept silent until he parked in front of a large cement and glass building. Another huge structure stood to the side with what looked like a giant golf ball on top of it. Her resistance began to disappear when she saw the rows of electronic equipment inside. Hal guided her through the lab and introduced her to the man in charge of the intercept program and to several other storm chasers.

The interested stares should have clued her in that Hal had spoken of her, but she became too preoccupied with her tour to notice. He took her out back to show her, like a proud father, what looked like a barrel with arms.

"This is TOTO." He fondly patted the cylindrical package of instruments. "It's the four-hundred-pound weather station we try to put in a tornado's path."

"TOTO?" she queried with humored skepticism. "Isn't that the name of Dorothy's dog in the *Wizard of Oz*?"

"Sure is," he replied. "But it actually stands for Totable Tornado Observatory. It's designed to operate in winds of two hundred miles per hour and therefore can go where we can't."

"Inside a tornado," Dana supplied for him.

After his nod, she inspected the awkward bulk of the precision machinery. On the outside it looked stark, but as Hal explained, inside there were temperature, air-pressure and wind-speed sensors as well as an internal battery and inkless recorders.

"How on earth do you lift this thing out of your van?" she asked while reevaluating his athletic build. No wonder he had such well-developed muscles.

"We don't carry it in the van," Hal explained with a hint of amusement that informed her he was aware of the trend of her thoughts. "TOTO is carried in the back of a pick-up truck, and I follow with the rest of the team. When we get to a site, we slide it out on ramps and hoist it upright. It only takes twenty seconds . . . then we get the hell away before the tornado hits."

A shiver raced down Dana's spine at the reminder of what they were trying to record. It always frightened her to think of Hal in front of a giant twister, but after listening to their exact procedures, she felt encouraged about his safety.

"What do you do with the information you gather?"

"We've never put TOTO exactly on target." Hal guided her to another part of the lab where a group of young university students were poring over computer readouts. "But when we get near enough, we collate the data we collect with the radar readings from the lab. This is the meat of our research."

They moved on to a wall paneled with radar screens. After introducing her to the lab meteorologist, Steve Kingman, Hal continued to explain the lengthy yet detailed process of their research.

The introduction to the Doppler radar captured Dana's interest. Because she worked in a plant that made Doppler radar, she understood when the two men described how it bounced radio signals from raindrops blowing toward or away from receiving antennae.

"These degrees of red indicate velocities away from the radar and the green show velocities coming toward it," Steve Kingman explained, his expression intent.

During Steve's display of several screens of data, Hal inched closer to Dana until finally he was peering over her shoulder. As his breath began to fan her cheek, Dana became less aware of Steve's words and more aware of Hal's presence. Her heartbeat jumped a bit when he leaned against her to reach his arm out in front of them.

"See that color shift where there's green in the red and red in the green?" He pointed to the center of the screen. "That's a sign of rotation. It means a tornado could be in that area."

Dana's mind became slightly scrambled with Hal's nearness. She could feel his muscles tense with excitement as he talked about his work. His eyes sparkled with enthusiasm and pride. It made her aware as never before, of what this research meant to him.

"Aren't you going to ask me how we know this?" He lightly squeezed her shoulders, making her almost forget what he wanted her to know. With effort she nodded her head.

"When we first noticed these, we weren't sure what they meant. But from the data we collected in the field, we realized they happened at the exact time and place we spotted a tornado. So now we know that they're the signatures."

Some of Hal's enthusiasm began to rub off. "When you see these color shifts, then you know it's a tornado and can warn people?" she exclaimed.

"It gives us a twenty-minute lead time for warnings," Hal replied. "But it's not perfect yet."

"If the winds come at the receiver from right angles they don't register," Steve inserted. "Also some thunderstorms display a circular wind pattern, but never become tornadoes."

"We still miss a few tornadoes and issue a few false alerts." Hal shrugged, but Dana could tell this bothered him deeply. "Overall, our warnings are fifty percent more accurate."

"That's a big difference." Dana wanted to assure him of his importance. "Certainly it helps people believe in the warnings. Perhaps they'll be better at getting into shelters."

"That's our goal for now," Steve agreed, but he heaved a sigh of a man facing overwhelming odds. "Hopefully with the aid of our research, we can predict more accurately in the future."

Dana looked around the room at the trained and dedicated men and women devoted to this goal and felt optimistic. Tornadoes were the most elusive phenomenon of nature. Because they formed at random and seldom stayed earthbound for more than twenty minutes, they were almost impossible to research. But these experts and students tackled the problem with purpose. Dana couldn't help but be impressed.

"Hal mentioned you worked at Brockwell." Steve intruded upon her thoughts with his question. "Would you be interested in helping out with the data collating?"

"I have to return—"

"There's a plan to install Doppler radar across the country," Hal said interrupting her. "The system is called NEXRAD—Next Generation Weather Radar."

If Steve objected to Hal's interruption he didn't show it. Dana listened with half an ear to Hal's description of the billion dollar plan and at the same time tried to figure out his purpose. Apparently he didn't want his colleagues to know she planned to leave.

A trickle of nervousness entered her system, but she shook it off. Absurd. They were friends—well, more than friends, but still . . . Of course seeing him at work was forcing her to change her view. As she shared Hal's dreams and hopes, her respect for him as a man grew. Along with the physical attraction she had already admitted to, this combination proved to be her undoing. Indeed, she believed she was falling in love.

Brought up short by that thought, Dana peered around the room. She tried to tell herself it was Hal's dedication that impressed her, but as she looked at the other attractive, intelligent men in the lab, she knew it was a lie. All of these scientists shared Hal's goals, but none attracted her—not like Hal did.

She followed Hal and listened with rapt attention to every detail he explained. But sometimes her focus centered more on the blunt-ended fingers with their dusting of chestnut hair, than the items he pointed to. At other times, the resonant tones of his voice pleased her more than the words he spoke. Always she was aware of the man.

Hal guided Dana to his desk, while keeping his hand at her waist. Her interest pleased him. He wanted her to understand and come to love his work. Her enthusiasm gave him hope that she would.

"So what do you think?" he asked as he seated her in his swivel chair. He perched against his desk and swung her around so that her knees touched his. He needed the contact.

"I think that you're a remarkable man, storm chaser." Her tone sounded sincere and her smile sent rivers of pride through him. "I admire your dedication."

"It isn't just that, you know." He wanted to be sure she understood every aspect, even if it might put his position with her in jeopardy. Love demanded honesty. "It's the thrill and excitement as well."

Her eyes clouded and a frown replaced the smile.

He took a deep breath. "You can't imagine the forces at work in a severe thunderstorm," he continued, staring deep into her eyes and willing her to understand. "It fills me with awe. When a tornado comes roping down from the sky, it makes you feel the mighty forces of the planet." In his excitement he bent over to capture her hands in his. "When the storm rolls overhead in giant mesocyclones and you see the mammatus clouds overhanging the prairie, you know a big one is coming."

"You love the lightning and thunder, too, don't you?" she asked and he could see true understanding in her eyes. "I used to love it when I was a child. I'd race to the knoll and watch the wall of clouds move toward us."

"That's a squall line that forms in the shape of a giant anvil." About to explain more, he stiffened with annoyance when a graduate student approached.

"Do you want to look at these stats, Dr. Underwood?" the young man queried, unaware that he had disrupted an intense moment.

"I'll check them later," he assured the youth and then turned back to Dana.

At that moment he realized he was holding her hands and he began to caress their softness. Her eyes sparkled with humor. So she knew he'd been annoyed by the interruption. He smiled and asked, "Now where were we?"

"You were telling me about cloud formations," she reminded him.

"Ah, yes," he became serious. "Did you know we're located along the dry line of Tornado Alley? It's the boundary where dry air from the Rockies meets moist air from the Gulf."

"Is this why your lab is located here?" she asked.

"It's one of the best places to study thunderstorms," he said. "So now you know why I'm here. It's important work and it's exciting."

"Aren't you omitting one thing?" Her voice held an edge of hardness he didn't expect.

"What?" Wariness crept into his eyes.

"The danger." She took a deep breath. "Admit you love taking risks."

For long seconds their eyes locked in a silent struggle. He wanted to deny it for her sake. She demanded he face up to it for his sake.

The air that was trapped in his lungs escaped in a whoosh. "Yes, dammit. There's that too."

She reached up to place her hands at the sides of his face and pulled it close to hers. He began to sink in the depths of her gaze. "That's part of you, an essential part, and I wouldn't want that to change."

His surroundings receded into the background as he became lost in the promise of her statement. Had he made progress at last? Could he claim her love now? Hope soared while her nearness clouded his thinking.

As he covered her hands with his, he pulled them to his chest and closed the distance to her mouth. He brushed a light kiss upon her lips and vowed in a low murmur, "I won't ever change. I'll always want you."

He pulled back a few scant inches and became lost in her sultry gaze. A creeping sensation along the back of his neck finally caught his attention. He knew people were staring at them before he looked up.

He cleared his throat, straightened and drew Dana up beside him. An urge to defend her prompted him to tuck her protectively at his side while he faced his colleagues head on. He squared his shoulders and forced his features into an innocent expression. "Let's get out of here," he whispered.

He left the lab with as much dignity as he could muster. The fact that some of his teammates had knowing grins on their faces didn't go unnoticed. All he could do was hope his public kiss hadn't embarrassed Dana. After settling them both into his van, he dared to look at her to find out.

Amusement danced in her eyes and her dimple deepened with her smile. He cast her a sheepish grin.

"I take it kissing in the lab is not a normal routine for you?" she teased.

"Especially not at work," he admitted and with mock chagrin continued, "I'll never live it down."

Strange as it seemed, he didn't really mind. He would've hated a show of emotion with any of the other women he had dated. But, he discovered, he wanted to shout his love for Dana to the world . . . and to her.

"Come here," he murmured, his voice husky with sudden desire.

He ignored her slight hesitancy and pulled her across the bench seat of his van to curve her into the crook of his arm. After tilting her head back, he placed a long draining kiss upon her lips.

"I've wanted to do this all day," he whispered against her mouth before taking it again.

Hunger flared with the force of a lightning bolt as he demanded her response. She opened her mouth and gave him her heated reaction.

Every sense focused upon the woman enfolded in his arms. Her heart raced as did his and her breath caught in gasps when he let them both take air. He couldn't touch enough of her as his hands roamed the curves he could reach.

When she traced her fingers across his shoulder and into the curve of his neck, his midsection tensed with longing. He wanted to make love to her and he swore she wanted it, too. But she needed to think about all she'd learned today. It was vital she absorb his confidence and purpose in his work. Tonight—tonight he would show her how much he loved her.

He made the promise to himself as he pulled away from the fragrant skin at her throat. With tiny nips and kisses, he worked his way back to her mouth and explored her sweetness. Her moan of longing stiffened his body until he strained with every cell. He managed to tear himself away.

"Let's go to my house." He traced a finger along her cheek and watched the cloud of passion clear from her eyes. He sighed and helped her straighten beside him.

"It's been a long day. We'll rest before we go out to dinner."

A smile creased her features and he reminded himself again of the virtues of patience. He knew a quiet romantic restaurant that offered dinner and dancing.

THE FLICKER OF CANDLELIGHT blended with the soft glow of the lights around the dance floor. Mellow music surrounded them as they swayed in time with the slow beat. An occasional glimmer reflected off of an instrument in the band, but it didn't disturb Dana's mood. Hal had her full attention.

Memories of his kiss in the van weakened her knees until he provided most of her support. She loved the rock-hard feel of him pressed against her. Beneath his silk shirt, she could feel the flex in his muscles as he guided her in time to the music. Across her back his hands rested, warm and sure.

She could imagine how they must look, alone on the expanse of hardwood floor. His tanned features contrasted with the white shirt. In black pants, he looked dark and dashing. With her mass of curls piled high with decorative combs and her filmy dust-pink dress she provided the wisp of color. They were winter and spring, hard and soft, male and female.

"Have you had enough dancing?" Hal murmured against her temple as one song blended into another.

"Never," she replied. She could stay in his arms all night.

His physical nearness wasn't the only thing that had her mind in a spin. While she had been resting earlier in the evening and thinking about all she'd learned of Hal, she'd come to realize one thing. She loved him. It was as simple and as complicated as that.

No matter how much she told herself that they were wrong for each other, and no matter how much she forbade herself to do so, she loved him.

This evening, this night and the next week were all that they would have—all that she would allow. The cost of loving him was high, but worth the price. These weeks had been heaven and she knew the next would be ecstasy. She refused to think about what came after her return to Los Angeles. One step at a time, she cautioned herself, and she'd take the full measure of each inch.

"Are you glad now that we came to the city?" He broke into her thoughts.

"I shouldn't give you the satisfaction of saying yes," she teased.

"But you enjoyed the day?" A hint of anxiety echoed in his rich drawl.

Her answer meant a lot to him, Dana realized. She could claim her revenge now for his treatment this morning. But the eager look in his eye changed her mind. She couldn't bear to destroy the glints of pride and contentment.

"I found the Severe Storms Lab fascinating." Although she wouldn't deny her enjoyment she could drag out her response.

"And?" he prompted.

"Your colleagues are very intelligent, dedicated and interesting. I can understand why you like to work with them."

"Dana." He squeezed her. "What about tonight?"

"Oh." She lowered her long lashes and then peered up at him with wide eyes. "The restaurant is very nice."

"And?" he prompted again, but this time the crease in his cheek deepened. He knew she was teasing.

"The dinner was excellent. My steak was cooked to perfection."

"And the wine?" He brushed a light kiss over her forehead, willing to play the game now.

Throaty laughter bubbled forth as she muttered. "Very mellow and dry."

"The dancing?"

"Nice dance floor." Merriment twinkled in her eyes. "The band is marvelous."

"And?"

"What else could there be?" She was all innocence.

"The company," he volunteered.

Dana glanced around the room. "It's a nice crowd."

The smile he cast her was eager and waiting. "And the present company?"

She feigned surprise. "Are you fishing for compliments?"

With an exasperated sigh, he pulled her close. His deep chuckles reverberated in her ear as she rested her head against his chest.

"The present company is the best part of the day," she murmured just loud enough for him to hear.

The band finished their number and Hal twirled her in a last spin before pulling her back into his arms. Her hips brushed against his body. Electric fire raced through her. Hal's intake of breath warned her that he reacted also.

He nuzzled his cheek against the sensitive skin of her neck and groaned. The animal sound of hunger and need tore at Dana's composure. Her fingers trembled as she slid them across his back.

Kiss me, her eyes begged in the dim light. Hold me tight in the safety of your arms. I want you. I love you.

Desire flared in the umber depths of his eyes. As if he could read her mind, he led her to their table. With suave courtesy, he seated her and then hunkered down beside her.

Eyes level with hers and tracing his finger along her cheek, he whispered in the muted room, "You're ready now, aren't you?"

She understood that he didn't just mean to leave. Taking a deep breath and allowing her charged senses to flow freely she nodded her head.

"Yes, I'm ready."

"I love you, Dana Jean Cunningham. We're going to go home now where I can show you how much."

9

SHE LOOKED INTO HIS EYES and read the tenderness and sincerity that mingled with the desire. She knew she didn't want to rush to the climax of passion with this man. There would never be enough time to savor the love he offered. In an effort to sustain the moment, she shook her head.

"Let's have one more dance."

"We can always come back." He smiled but he didn't pursue the issue. Instead he straightened and lifted the bottle of champagne from the ice bucket. "Another drink before we go back out there?"

"Yes." She was relieved that he'd made no argument. She lifted the crystal to her lips and wished she could prolong this night into eternity.

Her stalling didn't seem to disturb him, but it wasn't that easy for her. Her desires demanded to be released and it took effort to curb them. She tilted her head and smiled.

"What is it?" Hal leaned across the table and covered her free hand.

Dana lowered her lashes and set down her drink.

"You know I'm stalling." Her voice sounded husky to her own ears.

"It doesn't matter. We'll go when you're ready." He squeezed her fingers and his strength transferred through to hers.

"Do you have any idea why?" Her voice hadn't changed but her eyes implored.

He hesitated before answering. The atmosphere between them thickened. "I'm moving too fast. I know that. We need more time together...."

"No." She halted his flow of words by placing the tips of her fingers to his lips. "It's not that. I feel I've known you forever. It's that I want time to move slow. I want this night to go on and on and never end."

His expression held such tenderness that she wanted to cry. With a firm grip upon her hand, he pulled her upright and headed toward the band. "I can promise you that. Come. Let's dance." His voice sounded strained as he led her onto the floor. He turned her into his arms and whispered, "I need to hold you."

His breath feathered the wisps of hair at her temple, causing Dana to shudder. He tightened his arms around her and moved with easy steps. She settled her head in the crook of his neck and swayed to the slow beat. The wonder of his caring filled her empty soul. By the end of the dance she felt ready for his loving to fill her empty heart.

The drive from the restaurant to Hal's house passed in silence. But during the short distance, he cast her one glance after another, each one conveying his message of love, care and desire. By the time they entered the Victorian halls, she was in a glorious trance.

Like a spirit, she shadowed him down the corridor to the master bedroom. Her dress floated around her in a swirling mist, and their footsteps echoed in the stillness. He entered the room and reached to turn on the lights. Dana placed her hand on top of his.

"No," she said. "There's moonlight."

He didn't argue, but pulled her into his arms. He whispered her name over and over as he feathered kisses across her face and trailed them down to her neck. Her own desires mounted, demanding release.

With desperate urgency, she began to explore the shape of his shoulders, chest and back. With hungry lips, she sought his mouth and drained every drop of passion she could claim. Tiny sounds escaped as need and desire mingled. Her knees weakened at last and she clung to him.

"Love me," she whispered.

"I do love you."

Twinges of regret disturbed her passion, but she pushed them aside. They would only have this week and she refused to think how much their love was going to hurt in the future. She would take now and savor every minute. She stepped out of his arms and moved toward the giant four-poster bed that stood in the middle of the room.

Hal reluctantly let go and watched her graceful movement. If the lights had been on, he would have been able to read her expression. He knew her eyes would be full of passion.

A shudder of pure physical lust tore through him, but he clenched his fist against his body's demands. Her gift of love both honored and humbled him. He'd promised to take it slow tonight, but it would require every ounce of his strength.

She stood in the moonlight, her ethereal beauty framed by the dark mahogany of the furniture. Filmy folds of cloth prevented him from viewing all of her. He wanted to rip off her dress. He smiled. Someday when she knew him better, he would do that.

For now, he reached across the charged space between them and eased the chiffon off of her shoulders. His fingers shook slightly with the effort of restraint. He moved behind her and slid the zipper down with agonizing slowness. The muscles in her back quivered with expectancy, but he didn't touch. While his breath fanned the tendrils of hair at her neck, he slid the dress down until it formed a frothy pool at their feet.

Frozen in place, they both stood. The only sound and movement breaking the stillness were their shoulders heaving with their uneven breathing. Tension mounted until Hal almost suffocated from its thickness. He couldn't tear his gaze away from the classic line curving from the base of her tilted head down her spine to the rounded fullness covered by lace. Her golden skin silvered in the moonlight and he wanted to smooth his palms across the entire surface. Instead, he pulled the combs out of her hair.

A cloud of curls tumbled around her shoulders casting the scent of her perfume into the room. Hal inhaled her fragrance before stepping in front of her once again.

A moan emerged from the depths of his being. Expectancy shimmered from her. Love swelled with a force that almost drowned him.

"You are magnificent," he murmured as he took a step toward her. "I love you." He enfolded her into his arms.

She slipped into his embrace with ease, as if she belonged there, and indeed she did. With increasing urgency, he demanded with his kiss. She gave.

He lifted her and placed her across the large bed. For a moment, he tortured himself with a lingering look. With her hair splayed across the pillow she waited for him. Her eyes were dark pools of desire and trust. He locked her gaze with his and willed her acceptance as he eased the last garment from her trembling body.

Passion flared in her eyes before she wrapped her arms around him and pulled herself against his chest. "Love me," she begged again in a soft moan, raspy from longing.

"Don't move," he ordered as he took deep breaths.

Her body stiffened beneath his while she tilted her head to gaze up at him. He saw concern in her eyes.

"What's wrong? Did I do something?"

"No." He brushed a light kiss across her lips. "You make me crazy. That's all."

"And you don't want that?" She smiled.

He watched her dimple deepen, until with a shake of his head he spoke. "I want to go easy with you."

"I want to go wild with you," she told him while she traced the line of his shoulder until her finger moved down his collarbone.

His muscles contracted into fiery knots at the husky suggestion of her words. She moved beneath him, making him aware of every curve she possessed. His breath caught in his throat when she traced the contours of his back with the tips of her fingernails.

"Kiss me," she demanded and took tiny nips from his shoulder while waiting for him to comply.

Hal covered her upper body with hungry kisses. The woman taste of her made him ache.

"I can't get enough of you," he groaned against the flat smoothness of her belly.

"All of me is yours," she promised.

A force slammed into his midsection when she shifted to fit her body against his. He could feel the pounding of her heart matching the thunder of his. Her breath heated his skin as she gasped with each touch he placed on her flesh.

Her thighs felt like silk against the palm of his hand and each caress of the firm smoothness brought him closer to the edge of control. He nuzzled her neck while speaking words that were heated with his passion.

"You're so soft here." He gently kneaded her breasts with one hand. "And so smooth here." He moved his other hand along her inner thigh. "You smell so good here." He mouthed the fragrant curves of her neck.

With a slowness that cost him, he brought his hand toward the source of her womanhood. Heat melted his fingers until he felt the moisture of her readiness and it left him breathless. A groan tore from his throat into the stillness of the night.

"I want you," he ground out as he clenched every muscle for control. "I love you."

"Yes." She clasped her arms around his neck and held tight. Every nerve cell in her body screamed for release, and she held on with effort. She stifled a groan against his lips as he eased himself onto her, and when she parted her thighs electric lightning charged through her. Thunder raged within her when finally he joined them as one.

With each thrust Hal vowed his love to her, building upon their desire until they tossed about in a passionate storm. Their senses roiled like the dark clouds holding thunder, until they exploded with the wild fury of a tornado. "I love you." Her cry severed the last shreds of control and they reached the pinnacles of tempestuousness together.

SUNLIGHT STREAKED across the satin sheen of the mahogany bed when Dana awoke the next morning. Peaceful and languorous, she turned toward the source of heat beside her. Hal.

The night came to mind in a flash of steamy pleasure. She'd never been loved as she had in the past few hours. Never would she have believed that a man could take such care, yet burn with such fire.

Tenderness filled her as she reached across the pillow to smooth back a strand of chestnut hair. Even in sleep, power radiated from his body. She marveled at the way he had controlled that potency to assure her pleasure.

Love flowed in and out of her heart and for the moment, she didn't fight it. Later would be time enough. For now, she'd cherish the feel of a woman loved by a strong man.

His strength came from so many sources. Physically there could be no match. Lean and well toned, his form would be admired by any woman. But his strength of character attracted her more than his good looks.

Seeing him at the lab had opened her eyes to his dedication. Not only was he devoted to research but to sharing his knowledge to help others. He had to be brave and courageous to risk his life for such a cause, and she admired him for that.

All of the reasons she loved him crossed her mind. He'd made her laugh again with his warm sense of humor. His perception and sensitivity could patch and heal the broken pieces of her heart. His curiosity and daring had sparked her own sense of adventure that had lain dormant so long. Yes, there was much to love in this man. Once again, memories of the night washed over her and a sigh of satisfaction escaped her lips.

She turned on her side and snuggled against him. The hairs that roughened his chest brushed against her breasts. Her legs tangled with his and she delighted in their firmness. She stretched and smoothed every inch of her body across his.

She smiled when one eyelid popped open. He groaned at being awakened, but she knew he didn't really mind. To assure it, she began to caress every part of him. Both eyes opened.

"You're awake early," he commented with a yawn and then reached his arms up in a lazy stretch. He brought them back down around her.

"I'm not used to someone taking the covers," she teased.

"Oh." He quirked his brow at the comforter that blanketed her. His naked body was completely exposed. "It looks to me like you're used to having them all."

"Guess so." She chuckled, while sliding across his chest until she perched on top of him. "But I'll help you stay warm."

"Hmm." He slid his hand down her back to cup her rounded bottom. "I like the sounds of that."

Dana let the tendrils of her hair fall forward to tickle his face and neck. She kissed him. Sometime, during the minutes that she'd watched him sleep, she had decided that turnabout was fair play. He'd taken care of her last night. This morning she'd take care of him.

His muscles flexed beneath her, but she showed him no mercy. She blocked every move he made to shift positions. With deft fingers and moist lips, she tortured and teased until his aroused body quivered with desire and he moaned with longing.

"You're a tease," he accused when he tried to capture her lips with his.

Dana eluded his kisses, her lips brushing his mouth with tantalizing swiftness, moving across his jaw to his eyelids and then trailing along his temple. Finally she buried her face in the warm curve of his neck. Tiny nips of his flesh and nibbles on his earlobe sent shudders through his body.

Delighted with the reaction, she explored further. She traveled down his collarbone and found the soft whorls of hair. With fingers tangled in the silky fur, she teased him with kisses.

The contrast of his solid male flesh to her female softness fascinated her. She took her time in rediscovering all of the differences. With every touch, her heart raced faster. The woodsy smell of his skin tempted her. The sound of his breath coming faster sent her senses reeling.

His head twisted back and forth and she reveled in the power she had to please him. She wanted to make their love as tantalizing for him as it had been for her. In the process she found giving as much pleasure as receiving.

"I'm crazy about you," she told him as she nipped at his toes.

He started to pull himself upright, his arms outstretched to grab her. She rose on her knees, hands fisted on her hips and sent him a look of mock fury. But he didn't notice. He stared at the rise and fall of her peaked breasts.

"Dana. Come here," he groaned and cupped her fullness in his hands.

Her body reacted to his touch. She trembled and barely managed to resist his lure. Instead, she took revenge and cupped his fullness in her hands. His reaction was immediate and electrifying. He fell back on the bed, his breath jagged and harsh. She grinned.

"You're mine now," she warned.

"Always," he gasped as he arched into her grasp.

Dana's heart contracted. His response had been serious. She'd been teasing, *hadn't she*?

She leaned forward to study his features while her hands worked reverently against the weight of his flesh. He opened his eyes and stared into the very core of her.

"I love you," she whispered.

He reached up and feathered her lips with the tips of his fingers.

Suddenly Dana couldn't take any more of her games. With a boldness that surprised herself as much as him, she mounted his ramrod body. Then poised, ready to plunge, she waited.

"Now, Dana. Now." His hands gripped the curve of her waist. She covered them with her own and eased herself around him. The bedroom echoed with the sounds of his pleasure.

She performed a rhythmic dance that sent them both on a spinning trip of ecstasy. Her muscles drew his body into hers while her heart drew his soul.

Finally she lay sated on his chest. It took a while, but her heart began to steady and her breathing began to slow. She lifted her head to gaze into passion-sated eyes.

"Am I heavy?" she asked.

"Don't move." He lazily reached up and tangled his fingers in her hair.

Relieved, she placed her head back on his heaving chest. He was still in her and she didn't want to lose the intimate contact. She didn't want to ever leave this spot.

It would be pure heaven if she could make their every morning like this one.

"If that's how you're going to keep me warm," he murmured into her hair, his drawl filled with satisfaction and humor, "I can hardly wait until winter."

"You'll need an electric blanket by then." She smiled, her lips curving against the rounded smoothness of his shoulder.

"Don't think so." His fingers traced up and down her spine in idle slowness. "You're like a bolt of lightning."

"But I won't be here," she reminded him while tasting the saltiness of his skin.

Her eyelids began to drift shut. But her languid state lasted only a scant second. With sudden force, Hal rolled her off him and onto her back. She opened her eyes to be met by his stormy gaze. His shoulders loomed above her and the earthy muskiness from their lovemaking wafted in the air around them.

"What're you saying?" he asked, his voice husky with strain.

A cold chill raced across her heart as she realized the truth faced her now. No longer could she pretend a fantasy world existed that only held the night. Daylight had intruded and she couldn't lie to herself anymore.

"I won't be here in the winter." She spoke carefully and clearly. "You knew that, Hal."

"After last night and this morning you can say that?"

"Especially now."

"You said you loved me." He tightened his grip upon her shoulders and gave her a slight shake. "I heard you cry out in the middle of—"

"Stop!" She didn't want to be reminded of her abandon. Not now, when she needed strength. "It's because I do love you that I have to tell you I'm leaving."

He relaxed slightly as relief reflected in his eyes. "You love me then?"

"Yes, but I'm going back," she said, more to herself than to him.

"I have to live in the city by the university." He ignored her response and talked as if it was understood that she would remain. "But we could find a weekend place in Clear Creek. That way you could see your aunt and uncle and your friends."

"I won't be here with you." She repeated her stand, quiet desperation in her voice.

"Is it just the fear of storms or is there something else?" She saw the uncertainty in his gaze and the hint of vulnerability tore at her heart.

"If I stayed here with you, my worry about your safety would ruin our love."

"We can work this out."

Dana tensed. Her love wasn't enough. She had to make him understand. Before he could react, she rolled from underneath him and sat on the edge of the king-sized bed.

She pulled the sheet around her as she turned to face him. Her determination wavered when she saw the puzzled hurt in his tobacco-brown eyes.

"Get up and get dressed," she ordered softly.

"You can't run away." He leaned back on his elbow. "I won't let you. We belong together now."

Dana had to tear her gaze away from the sight of his naked form. Memories of every angle and plane were still too fresh in her mind. The imprint of his body against hers was too new.

"I'm not running away. Not today, anyway," she clarified. "It's my turn to take *you* somewhere."

He remained still and silent, studying her. Impatient and nervous, Dana began to worry. Her treatment seemed heartless compared to the tender love he always had for her. For a split second, she feared she couldn't go through with this. Perhaps running away would be easier.

No, she chided herself. It was cruel to treat him like this, but avoiding the issue would be ruthless as well as selfish. She had to make him realize that their love for each other could go no further than today.

The thought saddened her, because she had hoped for the rest of the week. But after last night, she knew another week together would make the end more difficult. Already, they both had paid a high price for their love.

She stiffened her resolve and bent to retrieve her dress. She prayed that what she had to show him would make him understand. Without saying another word and without daring to look at him again, she fled the bedroom.

A hot bath eased a little of her stress. But when she had donned the dark brown slacks and lacy beige sweater she'd worn the day before, her nerves attacked with renewed force. Fluffing the natural curls into a casual style and smoothing on her lipstick, she prayed to have the strength to finish this day.

The smell of bacon lured her into the kitchen where Hal stood at the stove with fork in hand. "Want breakfast before we go?" he turned to ask.

"Yes. Can I help?"

He handed her the bread and pointed to the toaster. His curt action hurt, but Dana steeled herself. With covert glances, she watched him finish cooking their breakfast. Blue jeans hugged the firm contours of his thighs and a red shirt accentuated the darkness of his coloring. The hunger gnawing at her insides had nothing to do with food.

They ate in chilling silence, both picking at their food. The tension thickened as she tried to ignore his glances of anger. This morning meal should've been special with tenderness and sweet endearments. Dana pushed away her unfinished breakfast. Hal didn't eat his, either. Together they cleared the table. After cleaning the kitchen, Hal held out the keys to his van.

"You know where we're off to. You can drive."

Dana took the leather case and thanked the heavens that her fingers didn't shake.

"Yesterday you brought me here to show me why I can love you." She took a deep breath and looked him in the eye. "Today I'm taking you someplace to show you why I can't."

10

DANA COULD FEEL his anger radiating toward her as she drove. She gripped the steering wheel and struggled to remain calm while his bitter hurt tore at her heart. She wanted to reach over and smooth his clenched fist with the palm of her hand.

"I don't believe this. How can you say we can't work this out?" he fumed while glaring daggers at her. He sat with one foot braced on the dash, his arm hooked over his knee.

Dana focused on the red dirt of the passing terrain and heaved a sigh. "You'll understand when we get there," she promised in a tired tone.

"To Clear Creek?"

"Yes."

"Something in your past?" he guessed.

"Yes."

"Something in your childhood?"

"My childhood was happy and normal," she reminded him. "You know that from George and Lillian."

"Why can't you just tell me now?" Impatience was reflected in his tone. "I'm not in the mood for games."

Dana slammed on the brakes and pulled off the highway. A touch of her own temper sparked with his in the close confines of the van.

"Do you honestly think I would play games with you?" She glared at him, her eyes flashing green with fury. "Don't you think I have any respect for your feelings?"

"Do you?" he dared to ask.

Dana gritted her teeth and faced downward. With unseeing eyes she stared at the countryside and called upon her reserves of control. It took every ounce of her willpower to calm herself down. Her heart thundered against her chest and her blood rang in her ears, but with firm resolve she kept her temper.

"I love you. I told you that, though I'm sorry now." Her voice echoed until silence fell around them. "Hurting you is tearing me apart."

"Is it Tommy? Do you still love Tommy?" he asked, but didn't look at her.

She stared at his profile and debated with her answer. Tommy was part of it, but not the way he thought. "I'll always love Tommy, but he's a memory now. My love for him is tucked away in a corner of my heart."

His shoulders relaxed a fraction. Dana waited, her breath caught in her throat.

"It's the tornadoes. You're still afraid."

"Yes."

A series of expletives erupted from the seat beside her. She ignored it and concentrated on the bright sunlight shadowing the rolling prairie and drew strength from the beauty of the blue skies.

"We've gone over the danger factors. You admitted the buildings in Clear Creek are safe," he said with exaggerated patience.

She knew his arguments were not going to influence her decision so she didn't respond. With calm purpose, she started the engine and pulled back onto the highway.

"You've seen the work at the lab," he continued. "You know warning systems are more accurate. You know what to do if a tornado hits."

Still, she remained silent, but she could feel the intensity of his stare. The facts he threw at her couldn't be denied. She didn't even try. They would be in Clear Creek in fifteen minutes. If she could hang on until they arrived, he would find out everything he needed to know. But it was a long fifteen minutes.

Again and again he explained the reasons she shouldn't fear a tornado until finally her patience snapped.

"It's not any of that," she interrupted. "I've told you before that I believe in everything you've explained to me."

"But you're still afraid."

"Yes . . . I don't know," she admitted. "Maybe if another storm hit I wouldn't be afraid now."

"But you won't take the risk and stay," he accused. "You won't even try to work this out. You're going to run away to California and forget I exist. Forget tornadoes tear through the country." He threw his hands in the air in exasperation.

"I'm going to try," she told him, but knew it would be impossible.

"Just like that?"

"As soon as George and Lillian return."

"You can't run away from life, Dana Jean Cunningham. There are dangers everywhere. California has earthquakes for God's sake."

Refusing to participate any longer in a useless argument, she clenched her jaw and drove through Clear Creek in silence. Tension hovered in the van, so thick she felt she could cut it.

A strange relief came when they arrived at the empty lot. In a few moments it would be over. But as soon as she stepped out of the van, she fell victim to a different sort of strain. As if she had opened Pandora's box, memories began to form, frightful memories that were painful and tragic.

"You see these flower boxes?" she asked, not turning to look at him but sensing he stood beside her. "I grew marigolds and pansies here."

She spread her arms wide and gestured to the empty space surrounding them. "A two-story house stood there. It was blue with white trim. It had a porch across the front with a swing."

"It can be rebuilt," Hal interrupted her. "If your parents want . . ."

"Will you listen to me," she shouted in a flare-up of temper.

He clamped his mouth shut and stared at her in stony silence. She placed her fingers at her temples and pressed the throbbing pain. She didn't mean to be sharp with him but the memories were tearing her apart.

She took a deep breath to boost her courage and continued. "This wasn't my parent's house," she informed him, her voice quiet with cold calm. "It was Tommy's and mine. We bought it after Sean was born."

If he responded to this statement, she didn't hear it. Caught up in the past, she began to relive that night. She stepped past the brick flower bed and continued the story as if in a trance.

"It was our first anniversary when we bought it. We'd been there a year, April tenth."

The weather had been humid, she remembered. Tommy had planned a surprise party and she had been disgusted that her hair wouldn't straighten into a pretty style. Besides that, the heat made Sean cranky and cross. How could a babysitter put up with that? To top it off she worried about a party she wasn't supposed to know anything about. She couldn't even ask Tommy to share her woes.

Woes! Dana exhaled with disgust. At that halcyon time in her life she hadn't known the meaning of the word. And what a time they'd had.

The party had been a success. All of their friends had been there. Harriet had even baked them a cake for celebration of their second anniversary. Champagne flowed while Tommy toasted their house, their love, their son, her...

They had partied until late at night. She barely remembered Tommy carrying her up the stairs let alone putting her to bed.

A cry tore from her throat. She didn't feel Hal's arms wrap around her and hold her close. She relived that night, so many years ago. "If I hadn't been sleeping so soundly I would've been the one to get Sean. He was crying you see, but I didn't hear him. Tommy did."

Giant sobs racked her body as she related the events that were still clear in her mind. "If I'd heard him sooner and gotten to him, Tommy wouldn't be dead. It would've been me instead."

Hal hung on tight to her trembling body. In a state of shock, he heard the story unfold. Each sentence brought him closer to a knowledge that filled him with anguish.

A chill raced down Hal's spine as the events of that night flashed in his mind. He turned and looked down the street at the sleepy town of Clear Creek. But he didn't see the rebuilt houses basking in the sunlight. His mind, playing tricks on him, focused on the destruction he'd seen that night.

Wind howled and rain pelted in a steady downpour. The leveled town sat in inky darkness. Flashes of lightning revealed row upon row of broken houses, piled like matchsticks and tinder. Twisted cars wrapped around uprooted trees in grotesque shapes.

Hal and his grandfather had arrived at the scene seeking shelter, but they'd found utter confusion. People were wandering the littered streets in a state of shock, looking for someplace to go. They didn't notice they were half naked and wet. Vivid in his mind was the face of the first man they stopped to talk to. Gaunt lines of despair creased his face while his eyes looked like empty sockets. He carried a sobbing child whose arms were wrapped around his neck and his wife followed, looking no better.

"It's not there," he kept muttering. "We went to the church, but it's not there."

Another bolt of lightning lit up the sky and Hal's grandfather sighted a part of the school building still intact. "Round up the wounded," he shouted to his grandson. "Send them to the schoolhouse. We'll start a first aid center."

By the time paramedics arrived from the neighboring town, a few able-bodied men were helping Hal to direct the survivors toward the school. They were guided by the constant flashing of red lights and the eerie wail of sirens.

A shudder tore through Hal. He blinked and tried to bring the present into focus. But Dana still sobbed in his arms, her speech broken now as she continued to try to relate her version of that night. He looked down at her trembling form against his chest and *he knew*.

Her screams still rent the air. He'd hurried toward the cries for help and found her, struggling with the men who carried the stretcher toward the National Guard's lorry.

"Take her," one man had shouted, "and get her treated for shock."

A quick glance had shown that those on the stretchers were past help. He'd grabbed her flailing arms and held her close to his body. She'd been cold as ice. Someone had thrown a large shirt around her, but it didn't protect her from the chill of her wet nightgown. With ringlets of hair plastered against her face, he'd thought her to be a young teenager.

He knew now with horrible certainty who that young woman had been. He closed his eyes and shook his head to block out the images. Chills raced down his spine and he held her tight, as he had that night so long ago.

His face buried against the tangle of curls, he wondered if she remembered who'd comforted her when her life had shattered into a million pieces. Someday he'd tell her that she'd been the one to bring his life out of the same agony to which she descended.

Her heartbroken sobs had touched a part of him he'd buried in the jungles of Vietnam. Her sorrow became his as he began to feel again, as his inner being slowly came back to life. He'd wrapped his coat around her and let her sob out her hysteria in his arms.

The lots were now covered with wildflowers instead of chaos. Hal realized it had been nearby where they'd sat. He lowered her with him and settled in the scented grasses in much the same position they'd been in before.

In spite of the warmth of the sun beating down upon him, the nightmare of that night continued to play in his mind. He'd held her like this, her form across his lap and her face tucked against the curve of his shoulder.

When her emotions had finally been spent, he'd lifted her up into his arms and carried her to the first aid center. He personally searched for a family member and had found someone. Thinking back now, he realized it must've been George. Assured she would be cared for, he'd continued with his rescue efforts.

But dreams of the young woman's sorrow and agony had haunted him for days. Those phantoms of the crushing grief suffered because of a freak of nature had been the force that changed his life. Even though he never saw the girl again, it had been her torment that made him vow to work toward the prevention of another such loss.

"Dana," he murmured as he brushed her sun-warmed hair with his lips. "I'm sorry—so very very sorry."

She pulled her head from his shoulder and looked at him with eyes dark and framed by tear-spiked lashes. "Do you understand now?" she asked, her voice shaky and her cheeks wet from her tears.

Hal nodded, thinking he did as the past blended into the present. But her next words reminded him of the future. His body stiffened.

"You see why I can't stay with you."

No, he didn't see. He didn't want to understand what she said. He refused to listen to her words.

"I can't go through that again."

He saw her mouth move, but he didn't hear.

"I don't want to lose another loved one to a tornado. I know life is a risk. No one is immortal. But I couldn't go through the same thing again."

She framed his face with her hands and pulled him toward her until their gazes locked. "Not with you, Hal. I love you too much."

He listened to her last sentence and focused on those words. Like a drowning man clinging to hope, he clutched at them. They loved each other. There had to be a way.

"Don't say anything more," he cautioned. "You're upset now."

"You must believe me," she implored. "You must understand."

The problem was, he understood more than she knew. But he wouldn't think about that now. Later, when their emotions were not charged with painful memories, he would figure out something. But even as he promised himself, he knew, deep in his heart, that there was little hope.

He tucked her head against his shoulder and advised her to relax and rest for a few minutes more. The scent of wildflowers drifted in the warm spring breeze while the hum of insects rang in the air.

Dana began to cry again and he tightened his arms to still the silent sobs. Tears had already been spent for her past loss, and he suspected this time she cried for the two of them. As he held her against his heart, he rested his head on the top of hers. A lone tear streaked down his cheek and glistened as it clung to her golden hair.

For some time they stayed there. Dana didn't know how long. Vaguely she was aware of the heat and the stiffness in her muscles. But she blocked it out of her mind. She didn't want to feel anything. There was only emptiness in spite of the loving arms wrapped around her. She tried to listen to the steady heartbeat against her ear. Sorrow for past events had been with her for years. She'd hoped there'd be relief in telling the story and getting everything out in the open, but it didn't come. Even her new love for Hal lay dormant and hopeless.

She tilted her head back and let the rays of sunlight dry the streaks of dampness running down her cheeks. She was so tired of tears, and it seemed more lay in store for her. She shifted stiff limbs and remorse finally stirred her. Hal must be paralyzed with cramped muscles. She looked up into his face to see concern and love in his eyes. Her heart did a crazy flip-flop and began beating again.

"We'd better go." Her voice sounded a bit shaky and husky. "Can you move?"

"Dana." He grabbed her shoulders and stilled her. "This doesn't change anything. I still love you."

She searched in the depths of his eyes and longed to find an answer, but couldn't. "I know," she told him, her heart aching with the futility of it. "I love you too."

Inside, she had always hoped that once Hal knew how she felt about her past, their relationship would end with a clean cut. But she realized now how impossible that was. She stood straight and reached out a hand to help him rise. After pulling himself up, he didn't let go, but brought her into his arms.

"Let's go to the lodge," he whispered close to her mouth. "I want to make love to you."

The scent of his breath and his sun-warmed skin sent shivers racing through her. Dizzy and weak, she ignored logic and met the demand of his lips.

"Yes, yes," she murmured into the hot darkness of his mouth. It would make the pain that much greater to endure, but she couldn't resist one last time together. Memories would have to last for another period of loneliness.

How they managed to make it back to the Walkers' quarters, she didn't know. She focused on Hal. She wanted to remember every small detail; the way his hair fell across his forehead, the angled lines of his face, the way his cheek creased when he smiled at her. Looking at him only made her want to touch him all the more.

Inside her bedroom, she didn't hesitate. Unlike the other times, there were no barriers to cross, no new feelings to explore. With haste and a touch of desperation, Dana pulled Hal's shirt over his head. His fingers didn't falter as he unbuttoned her sweater. In minutes, she reveled in the feel of skin against skin, flesh against flesh.

Falling across the bed, they entwined with unnecessary strength as if a mighty force would pull them apart. Dana searched every part of his naked body. She couldn't get enough of him. With fingers burning like fire, she tried to weld him to her—to become part of him so that nothing could separate them, not even the mighty twist of a tornado.

"Hold me tight," she begged him between frantic kisses across his jaw.

"I won't let you go."

Dana didn't pay any attention to the fact that his promise was impossible. Instead she clung to the words. For the moment she would believe in the fantasy.

"Love me forever," she implored.

"Yes," he groaned, his voice laden with yearning. "Forever."

He rolled her onto her back and emphasized his words with sudden aggression. Dana gazed into eyes that were dark and wild. She wanted to wrap her arms around him, but he had her wrists pinned above her head. Her body trembled while he positioned himself to possess her.

He paused. "You're mine, only mine," he promised and then he took her.

The room spun. She wrapped her legs around him and clung as they rode the storm of their passion. Lights exploded in her head—bright and primal.

"Hal," she gasped, when he finally let go of her wrists and she could wrap her arms around him.

"Hold tight," he demanded and then brought them both to the edge.

In seconds they stretched side by side gasping for breath. Waves of erotic pleasure washed over her damp and quivering flesh.

"You're wonderful," she told him.

A warm smile curved his lips. "So're you," he whispered as he traced the slope of her cheek to finally brush back a damp tendril of hair. "I wanted you so much, I couldn't hold back."

"I wanted you, too." She smiled to herself because it had been more like craving than mere want.

His smile disappeared and his expression grew serious. "I meant what I said."

His finger dropped down her neck and began the climb up to the peak of her breast. His touch sent sensations of fire, but his words brought a chill to her heart.

"I won't let you go," he repeated, his tone serious and determined now.

"You don't have to right now," she murmured as she placed her hand upon his chest. With purposeful strokes through his mat of hair, she attempted to distract him. She wanted to enjoy the magic for a little while longer, before the truth separated them forever.

With a firm grip, he stilled the movement of her hand. "I'm not talking about now and you know it." He spoke in a soft voice, but steel underlined the quiet tone. "There has to be some way that we can work this out."

"Maybe there is." She didn't really believe that but she wanted this conversation to end. "We can think about it later. For now—" she leaned forward "—for now, it's still my day off. Let's just love each other."

She held her breath and waited and watched while emotions warred within him. When he finally conceded, she reached out to kiss him and hide the relief that rushed through her.

The love they made that afternoon went at a more leisurely and relaxed pace. The urgency was still there, but they kept it buried. Dana didn't talk any more about the past. Hal didn't discuss the future. They just lived for the moment.

Dana knew her time of reckoning would come, but the longer she could hold off, the more memories she would have to store. She even managed to appear happy-go-lucky and normal during the baseball game she and Hal got roped into playing at the park.

Amongst her friends, it was easy to pretend all was well. Hal showed no strain as he joined in with the rowdy group. She even made a two-base hit giving her team the winning score. But her composure cracked when Candy and Bob teased them about becoming a permanent pair.

"What're you two up to over here by yourselves?" Candy strolled over to the picnic table where Dana and Hal stood talking. Bob followed close at her heels.

"Just talking about this and that."

"You convincing her to stay on in the area?" Candy asked Hal point blank.

Dana's breath caught in her throat as she glared at her friend. To be fair, she realized Candy would have no way of knowing how sensitive the subject was. But noting the gleam in her blue eyes, maybe she did.

"I'm trying." Hal reached his arm across Dana's shoulder and pulled her close to his side. She cast him a wary glance and wondered if he did it as a show of affection or to shut her up. Probably the latter she decided as he talked on. "She's a hard one to persuade though."

"Don't I know it," Candy shrugged. "Bob and I have been hoping you would."

"I'm working on it." Hal assured the Bradshaws and much to Dana's relief, the subject was dropped.

Not another word came up about their future, even during the late-night barbecue they stayed to enjoy. Hal spent the night and made love to her again and still nothing was said. The truce lasted through breakfast, but as soon as they stepped outside onto the grassy section of the yard, matters came to a head.

"It's going to be hard going back to work today." Dana stood in a patch of sunlight and stretched. Golden lights bounced off the strands of hair curling around her face.

"It shouldn't be too busy. It's only Wednesday," Hal mentioned as he surveyed the empty parking lot.

"Probably not," she agreed and placed her hand across her forehead to shade her eyes from the glare. "What're your plans for the day?"

He shifted.

Dana noticed an uneasiness about him. Her heart came to a stop as a sense of foreboding overcame her.

"I think I'll head back to the city," he told her.

"Oh." She cursed herself for being unable to hide her dismay. She hadn't expected him to leave before she returned to California. She wanted them to spend the week together.

"Will I see you again before I leave?" she asked.

"'Course." He nodded and her heart began thudding again with relief. "I've got to do some thinking. We'll work this out, I promise."

"There's nothing to work out," she reminded him although she wanted his promise to be true. "We've gone over everything. I can't stay here."

"I know."

"Then what is there to go away and think about? Why can't we spend what little time we have together?" She knew her request was selfish, but she made it anyway.

"It's too hard on you."

"Let me worry about that," she told him. Desperation crept into her heart now. She didn't want to let him go.

"Don't you think I have struggles of my own?" He rubbed his hand across the back of his neck and then looked at her. She could see the torment in his eyes. "Knowing what my job must mean to you . . . knowing I'm wrong for you . . . but dammit, I can't stop these feelings."

He grabbed her by the shoulders and pulled her body against his. The crush of her breasts against his chest reminded her of his strength. She accepted the hard kiss he placed on her lips, but already her heart cried out for him.

"I'm fighting for you, sunshine, with everything I've got."

With those words, he let her go and walked to his van. A strange combination of hope and sorrow filled her as she watched him disappear down the road.

11

DANA WALKED into the Drug Emporium and slid onto a stool. With her elbows braced upon the counter, she thanked the heavens that no one else was in the store. She needed to talk to someone and Harriet was the logical choice. Besides, Harriet made the best ice-cream sodas in the world and Dana needed cheering up.

"Hello there, missy." Harriet ambled down the service side of the counter. A warm smile of welcome brightened the lines of age on her face. "Harvey giving you a break?"

"He sent me down. Said my pacing was driving him crazy."

"Not busy yet?" Harriet commented more than questioned.

"I don't expect too many people until later this evening." She looked forward to the weekend crowd. It would keep her mind occupied with something besides Hal. Helping the cleaning crew, posting the accounts and even working with Harvey on the grounds hadn't kept her from thinking about him.

"What's your pleasure then?" Harriet slapped the counter with her hand.

"You have the makings for a cherry soda?" Dana asked, her spirits already lifting.

"Sure do and with lots of whipped cream, just the way you like it."

Harriet appeared at ease, but her sharp gaze swung to Dana more than once while she fixed the drink. Dana shifted, unsure of how to begin and if she even wanted to talk now. But leave it to Harriet—as soon as she set the frosty glass on the counter, she got down to the heart of the matter.

"Haven't seen Hal around. Not since I seen you two on your property the other day."

Harriet's comment hit like a bomb. She should've known Harriet would be aware of everything going on in the small community. Dana gripped the soda Harriet handed to her, but drinking it didn't cross her mind.

"I told him about Tommy and Sean," Dana mumbled, almost trancelike. "He knows now why we can't love each other."

"Do you honestly think knowing that'll stop your love . . . or his?" Harriet placed her fists upon her ample hips and scowled.

"No," Dana admitted. At least her love wouldn't disappear. It'd been tearing her apart for the last three days. But Hal seemed to have no trouble letting her go. Since that morning, he hadn't been in town or even called her on the phone.

"So, what did he say when you told him?"

"That he was sorry."

"No more?" Harriet wouldn't let Dana slide by with vague answers.

"He said he had some thinking to do . . . about us."

"Sounds logical. That kind of a load needs thinking about." Harriet came around the end of the counter and sat on the stool next to Dana.

"I'm sure he understands now." Dana attempted to smile. "It's best we don't see each other again."

"Horsefeathers," Harriet exploded as she threw her hands in the air. "I was sure the man had more sense than that. And so do you." She shook her finger at Dana.

If she hadn't been hurting so bad, she would've laughed at Harriet's typical antics.

"How're you going to fix things between you if you don't see each other for heaven's sake?" Harriet continued to rant. "You only have a couple more days don't you? When you leaving?"

Harriet's words didn't make the pain any easier to handle. She wished with all her heart they could work something out. But she knew, and Hal evidently did too, that it was hopeless.

"I leave in three days, Harriet. George and Lillian will be flying in Monday morning. I'll be flying out."

Seeing that Harriet was about to protest, Dana reached over and patted the older woman's arm. Before she could argue, Dana went on to explain.

"There's nothing to work out. I can't bear the dangers of his work and he's too dedicated to leave it."

Harriet sat for several moments and stared at her. Dana wanted to squirm, but she held her ground.

"Always thought you was a smart one." Harriet's tone implied she believed otherwise now. "And I thought he was, too. But it looks like both of you lost your common sense to the winds of that damned tornado."

"That about sums it up." Dana sighed and finally took a sip of her soda. In spite of its freshness it tasted as flat as she felt.

"What if he stops storm chasing and just works on the research?" Harriet suggested. "Have you thought about that?"

"Many times," Dana admitted, "but after the thunderstorm the other day, I don't know if I can handle it in the Midwest again."

"The fear goes away." Harriet patted Dana's arm. "In time you learn to live with the wind and thunder."

"Maybe for me, I wouldn't be afraid, but what if we had children, Harriet? Could I bear to see my child trundle off to school with storm clouds overhead?"

"Hal'd be there to help you through that. Besides, children'll find a number of things to do to turn your hair gray without having to worry about that." Harriet smoothed back a strand of her own silver hair. "Landsakes, look at mine. You younguns could find more mischief than a passel of monkeys. And that on a clear sunny day."

Dana couldn't help but chuckle at the older woman's reminder of days gone by. Days of happiness and well-being. She'd want her children to have a childhood that would bring them happiness. They were very receptive to their parent's fears. She didn't want to bring up sons and daughters who were afraid of storms.

"It's no use." She shook her head in dismay. "I've gone over that many times and come up with the same answers. I'm going back to California."

"You can't mean it, missy. Why, you love it here among your friends. Think of what it'll be like when George and Lillian get back. They want you to stay."

"My mind's made up." Dana stopped Harriet's words.

If the truth were known, all of Harriet's arguments had crossed her mind dozens of times. Dana could see no solutions even though she wanted to with all her heart.

"Has Hal suggested moving to California?"

Dana clenched her fists. In a secret region of her heart, she longed to ask him to leave his research and seek a position in Los Angeles. There were several fine universities there. But the logical part of her knew that to take Hal from his projects would be to take away part of the man. She loved him too much to do that.

"I wouldn't ask him to leave everything he's worked so hard for," Dana told Harriet as well as reminded herself.

"What if he decides?" Harriet persisted.

Hope flared but Dana didn't cling to it. Letting it sift away, she faced Harriet.

"I don't think he could do that."

"You'd be surprised what you can do when you love someone," Harriet said. "Mark my words, missy. You two'll come up with something."

With all her heart Dana wished she could believe that. Usually Harriet saw and understood more than the average person. But this time, she was mistaken.

Dana left the drugstore and returned to the lodge, but her mood hadn't improved. If anything, stating her thoughts aloud to her friend had only confirmed their truth. She prayed the weekend would pass quickly so she could leave Clear Creek. She had found love here, twice. Both times she'd lost it. It would be better to exist in a vacuum in the city than to suffer through this pain again.

HAL SAT at his work space and stared with unseeing eyes at the letters in his hand. They'd been sitting on his desk for two days now, but he couldn't bring himself to mail them. He read again the names of the top universities in Southern California. There was no doubt in his mind that with his credentials, he had a good chance of a position. But did he really want to go?

Looking around the research lab, where a team of students were collating data and radar screens were flashing, he knew teaching alone wouldn't satisfy him. In spite of the drudgery of putting together facts, excitement always lingered in the Severe Storms Lab. There just wasn't the same feeling of camaraderie in his office at the university.

Sure, there were eager students and research to deal with, but that was nothing compared to the thrill of gathering live data. But then again, without Dana in his life would there be any meaning left to his work?

Until he'd met her, he had been satisfied with his life. True, loneliness crept in once in a while, especially when he rambled around alone in the large rooms of his house. The aged mahogany seemed to cry out for the loving care of a woman and the laughter of children. And the instant he'd met Dana, he'd known she was the woman to fill in the gaps in his life.

But what were his dreams worth? For years he'd worked on improving a warning system. It was an effort that had brought him out of despair. Did he dare to let the dream go? Would Dana's love be enough?

His head throbbed from the mental conflict. He rubbed his hand across his forehead in an effort to erase the pain. Maybe he was making too much of a change. There were other goals to accomplish, other puzzles to solve. In California he could search for a new project.

He looked around the lab and focused on a group of fellow storm chasers who were listening to the broadcasts from the National Severe Storms Forecast Center in Kansas City. These men were every bit as well trained and devoted to the research as he. If he left, his work would carry on. That thought brought on depression. Nobody liked to think of himself as dispensable.

Steve must have sensed Hal's attention because he suddenly looked up. Caught staring, Hal shifted uneasily and finally stood. He tossed the letters atop the clutter of papers on his desk and strode over to his companions.

"What's up?" He tried to sound nonchalant.

"We're listening to the reports on the storm front in Texas," one of the storm chasers informed him.

"Do we have a team down there?" Hal asked, feeling guilty. He'd been neglecting his work these past two days. A storm line had been building. Normally he would have watched it closely in case it came within driving range. Obviously his teammates had followed its progress even though he hadn't.

Steve proceeded to bring him up to date, a hint of reproof in his tone. "We were going to send Clark, but decided to hold off. It's headed our way and most likely we'll be able to position our teams at closer range."

Having the teams near made sense. They could maintain radio contact and with the help from the Doppler readings on the radar, they had a better chance of positioning TOTO in the exact location.

Hal welcomed the familiar thrill. Without a second thought to the letters on his desk, he began to scan the scopes.

"How soon do they expect it to hit Oklahoma?" he asked.

"It should be in our area tomorrow afternoon," Steve informed him. "We'll send the teams out in the morning."

An air of expectancy hovered around the team of chasers. The men checked and rechecked their equipment while they kept track of the radar readings. Suddenly Hal was eager for action, but other emotions interfered. This might be his last chase if he gave up all that he had worked for and sent out those letters.

A shout from one of his co-workers interrupted his thoughts. "Listen to this."

The men gathered near the young man as he waved a paper in the air.

"We just got word from a television station in Abilene, Texas. A tornado touched down in a mobile home park outside of the city."

Dismay and horror flashed across the faces of everyone in the room. Mobile homes were easily destroyed. But wait. Why was the young man smiling?

"What else is in the report?" Hal demanded.

"Not a life was lost." The chaser beamed. "They issued a tornado warning. Thanks to our research, every person made it to the park's shelter."

A cheer went up. A lump formed in Hal's throat as he again saw his dream come true.

"A hundred people were in that park," someone shouted.

Amidst backslapping and rowdiness, Hal wrestled with his emotions. A hundred lives. The risks they had taken to place themselves in the path of the storm. The long hours of tedious collating and analysis of data. The effort had been worth this one moment of truth. *One hundred lives.*

And the sacrifices? Yes, what of the sacrifices, Hal wondered. How could he equate his love for Dana with one hundred living human beings? How could he be so selfish as to believe that satisfying his personal needs could make up for the loss of even one life.

Suddenly decisions seemed clear and the path, though rocky, was at least directed. With quick strides, Hal went to his desk and took the letters scattered across the top. Without hesitation, he tore them into shreds and tossed them into the trash can. Although his problems with Dana were unresolved, it seemed that a huge weight was lifted from his shoulders.

He'd been fooling himself to believe that he could leave his research behind. Years ago he'd made a commitment that had brought purpose to his life. That purpose involved too many other unknown souls to abandon it for his own personal happiness.

Hal set about making preparations for his team. He refused to acknowledge the smiles of relief upon the faces of his colleagues. They couldn't possibly know the turmoil he had been suffering. But they had seen his reaction to it and were obviously glad their old teammate was back to normal.

For one brief moment, when there was a lull in the activity, Dana came to mind. Her image wrenched at his heart as he realized he'd have to tell her of his plans. Not now. There'd be time to talk later, when preparations were finished.

He was tempted to ask her to stay. But he loved her too much to make the request. So in spite of the promise of adventure that lay ahead, part of him ached with sorrow.

THE PHONE RANG and Dana sighed with exhaustion. Friday night, and guests had been checking in one after the other. Another one calling now, she supposed. They'd been calling all evening with questions and demands. She should be grateful for all the activity to distract her, she thought, but a few minutes rest would be nice.

"I'm coming," she muttered as she lifted her tired body from the chair and walked with half-hearted speed to the reception desk. "Hello."

"How're you doing, sunshine?"

The sound of Hal's voice erased her fatigue. Alert now, Dana straightened while her heart raced.

"Are you coming for the weekend?" In spite of the fact that she knew he couldn't see her, she smoothed her coral dress.

"A storm line's developing. It's over Texas now and it'll be here tomorrow."

"A storm?" Her hands became clammy as she gripped the receiver. "Impossible," she insisted. "We would've heard a weather report."

"It's an unexpected development," Hal explained. "It'll be aired shortly."

Fear gripped her. Another storm? Here? With the phone cord trailing behind her, she staggered to the window to look out. There were cirrus clouds in the sky and trees were tossing about in the wind, foreshadowing a thunderstorm.

"I've been so busy I didn't notice the weather," she murmured aloud, unaware that she spoke into the receiver.

"Dana, are you all right?"

Hal's curt demand brought her up short. She shook her head to clear it and answered, "Yes, I was looking out the window."

"See anything?"

"Wind's blowing. That's all."

"Good. You'll have time to get to the city and catch a plane back to California." He paused. "You can wait at the house until your flight leaves."

"George and Lillian won't be back until Monday."

"Get Harvey to cover for you. This one's going to be big."

Leave? Go home? What about them—their future? He was sending her back to California—no questions, no plans, no promises. Just leave before the storm can frighten you again. She supposed she ought to be grateful for at least that much concern.

"The lodge is nearly full," she informed him, her voice sounding cool in spite of the turmoil within. "I can't leave now."

Hal paused. Dana could practically hear his mind churning. After she heard him take a deep breath, he spoke.

"I'll be over then. I'll stay with you and then take you to the airport Monday morning." He sounded protective, but there was something else in his tone.

"You were going out with your team, weren't you?" She knew even before she asked. It explained the long pause and the conflict in his voice.

"It's all right. I can go another time. You need me now."

Dana wanted to scream. Of course she needed him, but not for now. She needed him forever. His words gave him away. He planned to continue his research and to let her go.

"I don't need you," she lied while she tried to rally her pride. "You go with your team."

And she would pray every minute that he wouldn't see a tornado. But she didn't tell him that.

"It's not that important." He was lying too and she knew it. "I'll be there sometime tomorrow. We have some preparations I need to help with before I come."

"Listen to me, Harold Underwood," she faked a stern edge to her voice. "You're the one who's been telling me for the past two weeks how safe we are in these buildings."

"But that doesn't help when you're afraid," he reasoned.

"I'll have the guests here with me. I won't be alone."

"They'll probably leave in the morning after the weather broadcast," he reminded her.

That truth didn't bolster her courage. She shuddered as she thought about being alone to face another tornado, tempted to give in and board the next flight to California. But no. George and Lillian were depending on her. Besides she couldn't be sure all of the guests would leave.

"If I'm alone, I'll go stay with Harriet," she promised and the idea bolstered her morale considerably.

"You promise to go to Harriet's?"

"I'll ask her over here if I have guests." She had no intention of doing that, but if it eased his mind she'd tell the little white lie.

"Great idea." His voice brightened. "I'll go on with the team then."

Dana couldn't help but notice his enthusiasm. It only served to prove her conviction that she had no right to ask him to leave his work.

"I still want to take you to the airport Monday morning. I'll pick you up early so we can talk before the Walkers arrive."

She didn't want to see him there, at the airport. Goodbyes were too painful. "Maybe it'd be better if I just drove in by myself. We really have nothing to talk about."

An expletive crossed the wires making her wince. "You may have to do that if I don't return from the field in time. But listen here, Dana, we have plenty to talk about and we'll get to it even if I have to fly to L.A."

"What's the point?" All of her despair echoed in her voice.

"There're alternatives," he insisted. "We could work something out. You could live here in the fall and winter or I could live there."

"That wouldn't work. I'd still worry about you."

"It's not the best arrangement, but I do know this, Dana, I love you and we're just going to have to figure out something."

Dana didn't respond. Perhaps compromises could be made.

"Are you hearing me?"

Heaving a sigh of resignation, she responded, "We'll talk."

"Good. I'll try to get to you before Monday."

She sensed he was about to hang up and called out to him. "Hal."

"Yes?"

She gulped down the lump in her throat and whispered, "Take care out there."

"You bet."

"And Hal . . . I love you."

"Love you, too."

SATURDAY AFTERNOON Dana watched the sky. Lumpy mammatus clouds hung, forming a greenish-yellow canopy. From Hal's lessons on weather, she knew that these cloud formations signaled a tornado. Her tension mounted.

Odds said Clear Creek wouldn't be hit a second time, but there were no rules about where the twisters would touch down. She sighed. Were Hal's lessons really helping her? Sometimes ignorance was bliss.

She stared out the window and trembled as the force of the wind bent some of the trees to the ground. Behind her the radio blared. She listened with half an ear in case a tornado watch was posted.

Lightning streaked across the sky and Dana jumped back as thunder shook the panes. Her heartbeat kept time with the tattoo of branches hitting the roof as the wind tore through the yard with gale force. She pounded her fists against the sill and cursed her luck.

"It's not fair." She lifted her head and cried to the heavens. As the rumbles of thunder drew nearer, she wished with all her heart she'd listened to Hal and left Clear Creek. But it was too late now. Her body shook as hysteria began to mount until she wanted to scream.

"Hal," she sobbed as tears streaked down her cheeks. "Come to me, please."

She prayed that he'd hear her summons while she stared once again out the window. Lightning flashed, sending two jagged streaks across the darkening sky.

Thunder tore through the room, leaving Dana ashen and paralyzed. Her mind raced with images of Hal out in the storm. She could see his face, wet hair plastered to his brow, excitement glittering in his dark eyes. He would be shouting orders to his team and working to maneuver the awkward machinery. More care would be taken for the damnable piece of equipment than would be for their lives.

Dana wanted to scream at him to get back where it was safe. Chills raced through her body as she hugged her arms to her side, arms that longed to hold Hal. Even though she knew it wasn't best to be near the window, she remained, staring outside and willing him to take care.

The following advisory is being issued from the weather station...

Dana froze as the radio station broadcast the watch. She squeezed her eyes shut and prayed they wouldn't announce the area around Clear Creek.

...This tornado watch is in effect for Hinton, Fort Cobb, Clear Creek and Medicine Park.

"No!" Dana spun around to face the radio. "No, no, no," she chanted as she stood with her back braced against the wall and terror clutching at her heart.

She couldn't breathe. A mighty force seemed to be squeezing every bit of life from her body. Thunderous roars deafened her as blue-green flashes of light danced in eerie forms in front of her eyes.

Suddenly the door crashed open and Dana's heart crept into her throat. Hal! He'd come for her.

She turned toward him and froze. A man stood holding a child whose face was pressed against his neck. Behind him was a woman, her hair windblown and her eyes wild with fright.

"Did you hear the warning?" His voice seemed far away.

As if in a trance, Dana nodded.

"You have a shelter, don't you?" he asked, becoming impatient.

Again Dana nodded as she struggled with reality. Something about this man's presence was important. With effort, she pulled herself from the edge of hysteria and focused on the family.

The Swansons from cabin ten. It hit her with the force of a lightning bolt, and horror marched across her face; not everyone had gone home this morning. There were still two other cabins filled with guests. She'd have to warn them.

12

DANA FORGOT HER FEAR and guided the Swansons to the doorway leading to the cellar. After switching on the lights, she turned to the frightened family.

"Go on down. There're cots and blankets." She directed them in a voice that was surprisingly calm. "I have to make sure the other guests come, too."

"Is there room?" the man asked.

"Plenty," she assured him and then quickly described the facilities below. "You might want to start making coffee and water for hot chocolate. There're other children besides your daughter."

The family proceeded down the stairs. Without wasting another second, Dana dashed to the phone and picked up the receiver. Her hand froze and her breath caught. Dead. The line was dead. The wind must have blown down the lines. She stared out the window and realized she would have to go out in the storm.

Don't think about it, she told herself. She rushed to the door, but stopped when her hand touched the knob.

Thunder cannonaded as she peered out the glass. Electricity charged the air as it flashed in a mad pattern of light. Giant drops of rain pelted the dry earth.

She leaned her head against the pane and breathed deeply. It took a major effort to fight the urge to flee down the cellar steps. She couldn't go out there. Maybe Mr. Swanson would go.

As quickly as the idea formed, a vision crossed her mind. Images of the twisted bodies of Tommy and Sean flashed. That man had a child and so did the other guests.

With a spurt of courage she didn't know she possessed, Dana tore out the door and charged across the yard toward cabin two. Rain plastered her hair into instant ringlets against her cheeks. She brushed them aside and ignored the wind that whipped at her skirt and the bite of cold in the air. She ran until she thought her lungs would burst and her heart would explode.

She pounded on the door fighting her panic. Seconds seemed like hours until the Browns opened the door. A quick glance inside showed they had been preparing for a rainy-afternoon nap.

"Quick. To the shelter." The wind captured her words and carried them away. "There's a tornado watch."

In breathless haste, she explained where the shelter was located. Thankful that the Browns knew about safety procedure and would not resist her directions, she left them to gather their children and get to the main building by themselves. She braced herself against the wind and rushed toward cabin eighteen on the far side of the compound.

The blustery gusts of air pushed at her as if her body were a feather, and Dana leaned into the gale, beginning to wonder if she'd make it. It seemed that each blast of wind sent her backward as if refusing to allow her to warn the Cranstons.

It took every ounce of strength for her to struggle to the door. As if by magic it opened before her knock and a man grabbed her arm and pulled her inside. Dana leaned against the wall and breathed hard.

"What're you doing out in this weather?" Mr. Cranston asked.

"A tornado warning." She took another breath. "We have . . . to get back . . . to the shelter."

"No," his wife said from the bed where she sat huddled. "I won't go out in this."

"It's all right, honey," Mr. Cranston soothed, but Dana could tell he was as nervous as his wife. "It's just a precaution. We won't really have a tornado."

"That's not true." Dana wanted to scream at them, but she held her temper in check. "Clear Creek was listed in the tornado warning."

"Those warnings never mean anything," the man argued.

Dana could see he was becoming impatient and guessed it stemmed from nerves. She tried to conceal her own terror by grabbing their raincoats and tossing them to the couple.

"I'm giving you ten seconds to get those on and follow me out of here." She put her hands on her hips, not considering what a sight she looked with hair plastered to her head and rainwater dripping everywhere.

"Look here," Cranston protested. "You can't go ordering us around like this."

"I can and I am." She stood her ground. Outside she could hear the roar of the wind as its velocity increased. Her stomach knotted tighter as she fought the urge to run and leave these stubborn people behind. Knowing what could happen to them was the only thing that kept her there.

"If you don't come with me, I'll call the sheriff." The phone lines were dead, but the Cranstons didn't know that. The threat appeared to be working and that was all that mattered now.

Amidst grumbling from Cranston and whining from his wife, Dana bustled them out the door. Going with the wind proved easier and Dana thanked nature for that at least. With hurried steps they neared the lobby.

Suddenly a stillness settled over the prairie. A grisly chill coursed down Dana's spine. She faced the south-west and saw the ropelike funnel not more than four hundred yards away. Fear clawed at her heart as she watched the swirling of the devil spire. Her skin crawled as electricity lifted the hair on her head.

What began as a high-pitched wail built into a spine-chilling howl. Mrs. Cranston screamed at the same moment a mighty roar descended upon them. In panic, the woman started to run back toward her room.

Without thought, Dana suddenly flew into action. She grabbed Mrs. Cranston and dragged the fright-ened woman to the door of the lobby. Cranston fol-lowed just before the cars in the parking lot started bouncing around as if someone were jiggling them in the palm of his hand. The supersonic scream of the wind deafened them but she ran through the lobby, pulling them with her to the top of the stairs.

All three tumbled down the stairs and rounded the corner of the cellar. Breathless and windblown, they sagged against the wall. Dana's heartbeat still raced with the effects of adrenaline. She took deep breaths and focused on the shocked faces of the Browns and Swansons.

Tears coursed down her cheeks as she realized they were all safe. Too drained to move, she let Mr. and Mrs. Brown take care of the tattered survivors.

"It was so close," Mrs. Cranston sobbed hysterically, her short hair standing on end. "I've never seen a tornado before. It was horrible . . . just dreadful."

"There, there," Mrs. Brown crooned as she guided the woman to a cot.

For a moment Dana was deaf from the roar, but then sounds of other cries reached her ears. She looked up to see one of the Browns' daughters crouched on a cot, tears pouring down her rounded cheeks. Dana went to the child and sat beside her.

"We're all safe here. Really." She smiled and brushed away the tears with the corner of a sheet.

The child backed away. "You look . . . scary."

"It's just the wind. It blew me to bits."

"Just like in the *Wizard of Oz*?" Her eyes looked as big as saucers.

"Just about," Dana said and then silently gave thanks that torn clothing was all that they'd suffered. "But Dorothy's family didn't have a warning and we did. That's why we'll be as snug as bugs down here until the storm is over."

As she explained to the girl, she thought of Hal and his work. His efforts had just saved all of their lives.

And you Hal, what are you doing with your life? Dana closed her eyes and silently prayed that he was not facing what she had just witnessed.

HAL STOOD on a knoll and watched the funnel approach Clear Creek. His own brand of terror held him in its grip. He didn't even notice the shoulder muscle he had pulled when they had deployed TOTO a half hour ago. He didn't hear his teammates shouting behind him.

"Tornado, tornado. We've got a direct hit," a student called into the C.B. radio.

"We've got it on tape," another yelled. "We're videotaping from the tower camera. It's dark but I think we can catch the formation."

"It began under that cloud and formed a funnel, just like you said, Underwood."

Still the voices were a blur to Hal. He should've been elated that after hours of tracking across the back roads of the county they'd finally met with success. TOTO had been placed in the path of a tornado.

But no joy overwhelmed Hal. No sense of accomplishment thrilled him. He stood transfixed and watched the elephant-trunk twister approach Clear Creek. It snaked like a black shadow against the gray clouded sky.

"Dana!" he shouted. Without clear thought, he yelled at one of the students standing atop the van. "Get off. I'm going down there."

He had to get to Dana before the tornado hit. He had to protect her. He had to hold her in his arms and still the panic he knew she must be suffering.

"What the hell, Underwood." Steve came up and grabbed his shoulders. "You can't go down there."

Hal struggled against his teammate's strength. "You don't understand. I've got to get to her."

"Don't be crazy, man. She's safe and in a shelter. You'll get killed if you go in the twister's path."

"She's alone."

Why hadn't she gone to Harriet's? Ever since he had contacted the woman on the C.B. and discovered Dana wasn't with her, he'd been as edgy as a trapped bear. Now he felt desperate fear.

"You won't make it," Steve said, giving Hal a severe shake. "It's moving too fast."

Hal noticed his teammates staring. He returned his mutinous gaze to Steve and for tense seconds neither man gave an inch.

"It's lifting," shouted the cameraman, unaware of the drama below him. "It's going to go right over that knoll."

Hal tore away from Steve's grip and dashed to his position at the end of the van. His heart raced as he prayed that the tornado would dissipate before it reached the town.

The funnel danced in the air for endless moments, its tail trailing swirls of debris. Then in a heart-stopping flash, it touched down again to track northeast toward Clear Creek.

Too late. He'd never make it now. Hal clenched his fists as thoughts of Dana tortured his soul. She had clung to him in terror during the last storm, which had been mere rain and thunder. What must she be doing now?

Hal ground his teeth. He reminded himself of all that he had taught her, of how strong she was. She would use that strength. He had to believe that. As he watched, he willed courage and faith to Dana. He knew now, as never before, that she'd been right all along. He couldn't ask her to face this ever again.

The buildings and knolls in the distance blurred as a curtain of rain descended to block their view. Hal strained his eyes to keep the twister's progress in focus. Suddenly a vehicle approached the chase team.

"Has it hit Clear Creek?"

Hal recognized the male voice that shouted out of the half-closed window. He looked at Kevin Blake with new purpose.

"Not yet, but it's headed that way," Steve told the sheriff.

"You going down there?" Hal ran to the door and grasped the handle as if he could physically detain the officer from leaving without him.

"I've got to check out the town . . . see how bad the damage is." Kevin's voice sounded strained. Obviously he had his own ghosts to deal with.

"My team's committed to staying here. Take me down with you." Kevin hesitated and Hal persisted. "It's Dana. I've got to see if she's all right."

As if he'd said the magic word, the passenger door swung open. Hal tore across to the other side without a second thought to his companions. Steve could handle it from here.

Raindrops dripped into the confines of the patrol car as Hal hung on. Kevin raced down the highway. Neither man said a word. There was no need. They both knew about Dana's fear during the last storm.

"Do you think the town's been hit bad?" Kevin finally broke the silence.

"If everybody made it to shelters, I doubt there'll be much damage." Hal tried to believe his words for himself as well as Kevin. "It was a small twister. The buildings should withstand the impact."

"I pray that you're right," Kevin murmured and then fell silent again.

As the windshield wipers slapped against the rain, images tormented Hal: Dana warm and soft against his flesh; Dana with golden eyes and golden hair laughing with pleasure; Dana with past heartbreaks and the courage to move on.

Other memories gnawed at him also as Clear Creek's last tornado came to mind. He had found meaning to his life in the ruins of the first one. Would he find an end to all purpose in another?

At last Kevin reached the outskirts of town. He had to slow to avoid the debris littering the streets. Garbage cans rolled against the curbs, their contents strewn about. In one block, a child's tricycle lay in the middle of the road in a bent heap of twisted metal. They passed the post office where broken telephone lines wound like snakes in the parking lot. Hal began breathing again when he saw lights still flickering in solid windows and buildings still darkening the gray skyline.

"It didn't hit." Kevin began muttering in relief. "It didn't hit."

"Take me to the lodge," Hal said impatiently. He wanted to see for himself that Dana was all right. Even if she'd been physically safe, she might be suffering from mental stress.

Before Kevin came to a full stop in front of the lodge, Hal tore out of the car. He waved a quick thanks and charged into the lodge, slamming open the doors as he went.

"Dana!" he shouted to the empty silence. In a mad dash he thundered down the stairs only to confront a group of startled faces.

"Hal, what are you doing here?"

Dana unfolded herself from a cot, a small child in her arms. Her dress was tattered and her hair windblown, but she looked warm, healthy and wonderfully normal.

A whoosh of air escaped his burning lungs as he sank down on the end of her cot. He didn't dare speak. He gripped the blankets so that she wouldn't see the way his hands shook and simply stared, taking in the sight of her.

Dana sat back down and watched Hal struggle for inner control. Something terrible had upset him and she waited with growing dread for what his news would be. The child in her arms became restless and Dana whispered, "Go to your mommy now." As the girl scampered to her parents, Dana noticed the others were waiting anxiously to hear Hal's news.

She placed her hand on his arm and squeezed it to let him know that whatever he had to tell them, they were ready.

"What's it like out there?" Her voice shook slightly. "Were there any lives lost? Did the tornado destroy the town?"

"It didn't hit," Hal finally spoke, his voice husky and low.

"But we saw..."

"I hoped you hadn't." He suddenly reached for her and pulled her close.

Smothered against the damp shirt under his open raincoat she tried to respond. Before she could, the group began to tell him what had happened.

"And she saved our lives," Bertha Cranston concluded.

A little embarrassed by the praise, Dana stopped resisting Hal's embrace and remained buried against him. Besides, it was heaven to feel his arms around her and to know he was safe. Then it occurred to her to wonder why he wasn't with his team. Lifting her head, she asked him.

"We saw the tornado, too," he told her. "We managed to get TOTO in its path, but then we saw the funnel heading toward Clear Creek." He took a deep breath.

It was her turn to hold him as he related the events of the past few hours. His underlying concern touched her deeply. She knew that feeling well. Hadn't she just spent the last hour worrying about him?

"So that's all I really know about the shape of the town," he admitted. "Blake brought me straight to the lodge."

"I'm sure everyone is safe in a shelter somewhere," she assured their group. "After what this town has been through, no one's going to ignore the warnings."

Dana couldn't help but notice the rather sheepish expressions on the faces of the Cranstons. They weren't likely to forget their close call.

"Can we go back up now?" Naomi Brown asked. The rest of the group waited for Hal's reply.

"No. The warnings are still posted." He rubbed the back of his neck. "That twister missed, but others could form." He looked up and around the large room. "You do have the battery-operated radio, don't you?"

Ben Swanson turned the volume back up to where it had been until Hal's arrival. The broadcaster reported several tornado sightings and the group gathered around the counter to listen. Once the others were occupied, Dana took advantage of the semiprivacy and motioned to Hal.

"Come, let's go sit in that corner," she whispered. "I want to talk to you."

Hal shed his raincoat and followed her. She ached with awareness. She wanted to hold him close and tell him of her love. Instead she sat, with outward calm, upon the edge of the farthest cot.

"I was so worried about you," he murmured.

"I was afraid at first," she admitted. "Terribly afraid. But then things got too busy."

Her poise didn't quite come off. Hal reached out and cupping her cheek, he tilted her head back. He gazed into her eyes and she let him see every emotion she'd experienced during that awful time.

"I'm so sorry you had to go through that," he whispered.

Dana placed her hand over his. "There's nothing to be sorry for."

"I should've insisted that you get on that plane."

"Then I never would've known, would I?" She started to explain, but he interrupted.

"I'll take you to the airport Monday morning. I promise."

He wasn't listening to her. Dana tugged his hand into her lap and gave it a slight shake.

"I'll go to the airport with you," she informed him. "And I'll fly to L.A." She saw the pain flicker in his eyes, and her heart melted. "I have to go back to turn in my resignation and close out my affairs. My apartment needs to be sublet, but I can probably be back within a month's time."

From the comical expression on his face, she guessed he might be in a state of shock. She understood. The decisions she'd made this past hour had shaken her up a bit, too.

"Of course I'd really like you to come to L.A. if you can. At least long enough to meet my parents. We could get married there and fly back to Oklahoma."

"Married?" He stared in disbelief. "I want that more than anything in this world. But you . . . what about you?"

"Hal, I faced that tornado. I didn't think I could," she admitted, still a little in awe of herself. "And when we were all safe, here in the cellar, everyone was still frightened. So I explained to them all the things you taught me. I started believing."

"There're no guarantees," he reminded her as he brushed a tendril of hair behind her ear. "You might have to face this again."

"But I can," she assured him. "I just did."

"It's a big step. And I want you to stay. But you must be sure. You were fortunate this time and made it to a shelter."

"Yes, thanks to you and the work you're doing. We had the warning."

"They aren't always accurate."

She realized he had her best interests in mind. He needed to know that she was certain of her feelings.

"That's why I want to help," she told him.

"Help?" he queried, his eyebrows raised. At least the frown had disappeared and a flicker of hope lit his eyes.

"I understand now, what your work means to you," she explained. "I want to be a part of it. I want to help at the lab."

"I don't know what to say." He let go of her hand and traced his finger down her cheek.

"Say yes," she whispered and smiled up at him.

One of the Browns' children began to cough. In surprise, Dana focused on the rest of the group. She'd forgotten they were there. But evidently the others were well aware of the presence of the couple. Dana was too happy to be embarrassed.

A silly grin deepened the dimple in her cheek. Hal saw it and looked up too. He glanced back at her and they shared a secret look before he addressed the curious group.

"Good news, folks," he announced. "Dana's going to be my wife."

They cheered and congratulated and then with good grace, they became absorbed once again in the radio, leaving the two of them as much privacy as they could.

"You're my sunshine," he whispered. "You'll bring warmth and happiness to my life."

"Probably a few storms too," she teased.

Pulling her close, he bent to kiss her, murmuring, "But then, you know how much I love to chase them."

BETRAYALS. DECISIONS AND CHOICES...

BUY OUT by David Wind   £2.95

The money-making trend of redeveloping Manhattan tenement blocks sets the scene for this explosive novel. In the face of shady deals and corrupt landlords, tenants of the Crestfield begin a fight for their rights – and end up in a fight for their lives.

BEGINNINGS by Judith Duncan   £2.50

Judith Duncan, bestselling author of "Into the Light", blends sensitivity and insight in this novel of a woman determined to make a new beginning for herself and her children. But an unforeseen problem arises with the arrival of Grady O'Neil.

ROOM FOR ONE MORE by Virginia Nielsen   £2.75

At 38, Charlotte Emlyn was about to marry Brock Morley – 5 years her junior. Then her teenage son announced that his girlfriend was pregnant. Could Brock face being husband, stepfather *and* grandfather at 33? Suddenly 5 years seemed like a lifetime – but could the dilemma be overcome?.

These three new titles will be out in bookshops from MAY 1989

W❀RLDWIDE

AROUND THE WORLD WORDSEARCH
COMPETITION!

How would you like a years supply of Mills & Boon Romances ABSOLUTELY FREE? Well, you can win them! All you have to do is complete the word puzzle below and send it in to us by October 31st. 1989. The first 5 correct entries picked out of the bag after that date will win **a years supply of Mills & Boon Romances** (*ten books every month - **worth around £150***) What could be easier?

```
R D N A L R E Z T I W S
E O N M C H I N A A C C
G M U I G L E B N N U O
Y E C E G W H I Z C B T
P D R H S E R I A Z A L
T N S M P E R U N D D A
N A W I A T P I I E N N
Y L A T I N A N A N A D
N G S T N H Y D E M L Q
W N O J A M A I C A L A
R E L A D A N A C R O R
T H A I L A N D D K H I
```

ITALY	THAILAND	SCOTLAND	SWITZERLAND
GERMANY	IRAQ	JAMAICA	
HOLLAND	ZAIRE	TANZANIA	
BELGIUM	TAIWAN	PERU	
EGYPT	CANADA	SPAIN	
CHINA	INDIA	DENMARK	
NIGERIA	ENGLAND	CUBA	

PLEASE TURN OVER FOR DETAILS ON HOW TO ENTER ▶

HOW TO ENTER

All the words listed overleaf, below the word puzzle, are hidden in the grid. You can find them by reading the letters forward, backwards, up or down, or diagonally. When you find a word, circle it or put a line through it, the remaining letters (which you can read from left to right, from the top of the puzzle through to the bottom) will spell a secret message.

After you have filled in all the words, don't forget to fill in your name and address in the space provided and pop this page in an envelope (you don't need a stamp) and post it today. Hurry - competition ends October 31st. 1989.

Mills & Boon Competition,
FREEPOST,
P.O. Box 236,
Croydon,
Surrey. CR9 9EL

Only one entry per household

Secret Message _____

_____

Name _____

Address _____

_____

_____

_____ Postcode _____

You may be mailed as a result of entering this competition

MAILING PREFERENCE SERVICE

COMP 6